S0-BRG-119

06/19/05
Primary Source
Dm
1-CIRCS nd.

avid S.
eft

ormation Concepts Incorporated

8·46

TATISTICAL ANALYSIS

FOR

AREAL DISTRIBUTIONS

LIBRARY
SEMINOLE COMMUNITY COLLEGE

REC. NOV 4 1975

SANFORD, FLORIDA
32771

Monograph Series
Number Two

Benjamin H. Stevens, Editor

REGIONAL SCIENCE RESEARCH INSTITUTE
G.P.O. Box 8776, Philadelphia, Pennsylvania 19101

Copyright © 1966 by David S. Neft

All Rights Reserved

Printed in the United States of America

To

L. N. and W. W.

ACKNOWLEDGEMENTS

This study was written as part of the American Geographical Society's Macrogeography Project and it is intended primarily for geographers and other social scientists who are concerned with the analysis of areal distributions. While there is a notable absence of complicated mathematics in this work, it is assumed that the reader has a basic knowledge of linear statistics, at a level roughly equivalent to the mastering of such books as *Statistical Inference* by Walker and Lev and *Introduction to Statistical Analysis* by Dixon and Massey.

There are many people who have generously devoted much time and effort to make this study possible, although I alone am responsible for all errors in the manuscript. Frederick E. Croxton, Professor Emeritus of statistics at Columbia College, and Alfred J. Kana, former Associate in statistics at Columbia College, stimulated my interest in the study of statistics and, as part of a senior seminar, sent me to work at the American Geographical Society. This marked the beginning of a very happy association. Charles B. Hitchcock, Director of the society, encourages staff members to present new ideas and concepts and to pursue their own research ideas. Thus, during the five years that I worked there, the society provided me with intellectual opportunity and freedom, as well as financial support for this study. I am also indebted to O. M. Miller, Assistant Director of the society, for his active support of this research and for permission to use his very clever and topical short poem (see p. 147).

The person who has had the greatest influence on this study is William Warntz, Research Associate at the American Geographical Society and at Princeton University, and supervisor of the society's Macrogeography Project. He is responsible for arousing my interest in the application of statistical methods to problems in geography, and his guidance, suggestions, and criticisms have been of immeasurable value to this work. In addition, I am grateful to Dr. Warntz for his permission to use the file of data for the Macrogeography Project which contains much unpublished material compiled by Dr. Warntz and myself.

Another man whose influence is reflected in this study is John Q. Stewart, Professor Emeritus of astronomical physics at Princeton University and the guiding genius of the Social Physics Group there. The macrogeographic approach, one of the bases of this work, stems from Stewart's formulation of the modern concept of Social Physics.

The committee which reviewed this manuscript as a doctoral dissertation at Columbia University was headed by Robert Parker Eastwood, Professor of statistics at the Columbia Graduate School of Business, and his strenuous efforts in my behalf are deeply appreciated.

Others who have generously offered helpful suggestions and clarifications include Robert Harris of the Department of Health, Education, and Welfare, Professor David L. Wallace of the University of Chicago, and Professor Benjamin Stevens of the University of Pennsylvania and the Regional Science Research Institute. Valuable computational assistance was provided by Allan Nelson and Roger Ring of the Department of Defense.

This study also has been aided by cooperation from other individuals and organizations. My thanks go to the editors of the *Journal of Regional Science* for permission to use *Tables 8* and *9* which originally appeared in that periodical in an article by Warntz and Neft, and to the editor of the *Geographical Review* for permission to use Mr. Miller's poem. Finally, the whole Macrogeography Project, and this work in particular, has benefited from the close cooperation which exists between the American Geographical Society and the United States Bureau of the Census.

The efforts of several members of the American Geographical Society's staff were instrumental in transforming this study from a research project into a finished manuscript. William Briesemeister and Douglas Waugh offered suggestions regarding the presentation of the maps and charts, which were drafted by Mr. Waugh. John Macisco and Evlin Friedman supplied some of the labor power for the boring task of calculating the values for many of the applications that appear in this work. Mrs. Inez Chaney typed much of the manuscript.

Last, but of course not least, I am indebted to my wife, Naomi, who edited the final Manuscript and to Mrs. Sue Neft, who did most of the typing and proof reading of the original manuscript.

Cover photograph courtesy of American Geographical Society.

TABLE OF CONTENTS

TABLE OF CONTENTS (Cont)

TABLE OF CONTENTS (Cont)

LIST OF TABLES

LIST OF TABLES (Cont)

LIST OF ILLLUSTRATIONS

LIST OF ILLUSTRATIONS (Cont)

Figure   Page

LIST OF ILLUSTRATIONS (Cont)

CHAPTER I
THE RELATIONSHIP BETWEEN STATISTICS AND GEOGRAPHY

INTRODUCTION

The history of scientific achievement has shown that the greatest advances in a field occur only after fears about increasing the level of abstraction have been discarded. Many of these achievements have been in the form of quantitative macroscopic generalizations. Unfortunately, some men still believe that since all people are distinct individuals and every portion of the earth's surface is different from every other portion, one cannot generalize. Nowhere in the physical or social sciences is this attitude more prevalent than in the field of geography. This attitude of many well-known geographers is one of the causes of the slow theoretical development of the subject for the last generation. It is also undoubtedly related to the fact that many leading colleges and universities, including Harvard, have eliminated geography courses from their curricula.

Recently several geographers have expressed their dissatisfaction with this situation and have proposed additions to the more traditional methods of geographic analysis. An excellent example of this is provided by the suggestions of Edward A. Ackerman [1], Executive Officer of the Carnegie Institution of Washington:

"First, thorough analysis of the nature of two-dimensional distributions *in the abstract* should be able to furnish a theoretical framework with capacity to illuminate actually observed distributional patterns and space relations. Such a theoretical framework is probably as important at this time as definition of the earth's physical matrix for observation was at an earlier stage in the science. Geography thus far has been notably weak in its attention to this possible building block. While the science has a voluminous literature on methodology and procedure, geographers have done comparatively little toward considering their subject in the abstract. This is in notable contrast to economics. That discipline has a well-cultivated field of abstract theory, from which both understanding and sharpened analytical tools have emerged.

The possibilities of studying areal distributions in the abstract may be illustrated briefly by reference to the attributes of such distributions. Abstractly considered the phenomenal content of space shows the following: (1) It is generically classifiable. (2) Any given class (or classes) of phenomena show attributes of: (a) density; (b) agglomeration and scatter; (c) extent; (d) orientation; and (e) shape, including skewness from a node (if one exists). (3) Two or more classes of phenomena may show correlation or covariance."

One necessary tool for a useful increase in the level of abstraction in a social science is the development of a body of statistical and mathematical techniques specifically designed for the problems found in that social science. While it is true that statistics can never prove anything, statistical methods can be used for many worthwhile purposes. Among these are the description of an unwieldy number of observations by a few simple parameters, the reduction and measurement of uncertainty through the use of carefully designed statistical tests of hypotheses, the estimation of the characteristics of a population from sample statistics, the prediction of future patterns from the values of measures computed for past and present distributions, and the formulation of general theories of aggregate behavior based on the regularities among distributions which are occasionally revealed by comparing the values of certain statistical parameters.

Statistical methods to serve the needs of the particular discipline have been developed, and are continually being improved, for most of the social sciences. To realize the great extent of this development, one merely has to read some of the recent literature in economics, sociology, or psychology. Unfortunately, little has been done in the field of geography. It is the contention here that better statistical methods for geography are necessary, although not sufficient, for progress in the subject. This study is intended to be a start in this direction. The aim of this work is to present the basis of a complete, simple, integrated system of statistical methods for the analysis of phenomena that are distributed over an area. In addition to the introduction of many new measures, there will be an attempt to coordinate previous work in the field by emphasizing the relationships among various techniques and by proposing a standardized, internally consistent system of notation.

This work consists of four basic parts, which follow a brief review of past contributions to the field. The system of areal distributions and moments which are the basis of most of this study will be developed in Chapters II and III. Descriptive measures for analyzing areal populations and certain basic model surfaces are discussed in Chapters IV through VII. The application of techniques of correlation analysis to areal problems is treated in Chapter VIII. Finally some methods for drawing inferences from areal samples are proposed in Chapter IX.

This set of statistical methods for areal distributions is not intended to be a system that is isolated from the physical world. Rather, the aim is to promote empirical investigation of socio-economic phenomena. There are four basic types of practical applications of these methods. One is the study of the areal distribution of a variable in a region over a period of time in order to predict the future areal distribution of that variable. This has considerable usefulness in all forms of planning, both for business and government. In Chapters IV and VII the history of the distribution of population in the United States will be used to illustrate the analysis of areal distributions over time. The data from each of the 18 censuses of the United States were used in this analysis and the area considered was the area of the continental United States at each census.[1] Alaska, Hawaii, Puerto Rico, and other U.S. possessions have been excluded (see p. 18). Since data are available for the latter part of the colonial period, census counts and estimates for the years 1754 and 1775 were also included.[2] For these dates,

[1]U. S., Bureau of the Census [107].

[2]U. S., Bureau of the Census [104], pp. 4-15, 149-185, Sutherland [98].

the area was considered to be that part of the United States in 1790 which was under English rule in the colonial year. For the period prior to 1754, data are too scanty and unreliable to be useful.

The second basic type of application is the investigation of the relationships among the areal distributions of variables in a region at a given time. This type of analysis is particularly suited to the field of marketing. A typical study might involve a comparison among the areal distributions of a firm's or industry's raw materials, plant locations, and potential market. Similar studies will be illustrated in Chapter VIII.

In addition, it is possible to compare the areal patterns of a variable among several regions. Before a geographer, economist, or historian can explain the causes of differences in the areal pattern of phenomena among many regions, he must have ways of measuring the nature and extent of such differences. Some suitable methods for this purpose are proposed in Chapters IV through VII. As examples of this approach, the areal distributions of population for seven nations will be studied. The seven nations included are Australia, Brazil, China, India, Japan, the United Kingdom, and the United States.[3] It must be emphasized that although human populations of countries are being illustrated, these methods could be used to examine any statistical population that is distributed over any area.

Finally, a sample can be studied and values of parameters can be inferred from an analysis of statistics calculated from the sample observations. Such procedures will be discussed in Chapter IX and hypotheses will be tested, using statistics computed from several actual areal samples.

Thus, all the methods that are to be discussed in subsequent chapters will be illustrated by using them to analyze actual areal distributions.

CURRENT METHODS OF STATISTICAL ANALYSIS OF GEOGRAPHIC DATA

Although most geographers and statisticians are content to go their separate ways, both groups have been developing and applying methods for quantitative analysis of geographic data. In addition, many economists, sociologists, ecologists, and other social scientists are now making contributions to this field. While a complete bibliography of these contributions is beyond the scope of this study, a summary and classification of some of the major developments are in order.

Linear Statistical Methods Applied to Geographic Data

Many geographers recently have been applying some of the familiar methods of linear statistics to geographic problems. Unfortunately, some of these

3Data From:
  Australia, Commonwealth Bureau of Census and Statistics [4].
  Brazil, Conselho Nacional de Estatistica [11].
  Great Britain, General Register Office [41].
  Japan, Bureau of Statistics [54, 55].
  U. S., Bureau of the Census [107], 1960.
  Steinberg [85].

individuals too frequently succeed only in revealing their lack of training in statistics. Perhaps the classic example of this is Weaver [120] who, while calling for improved methods of quantitative analysis for geography, has proceeded to misuse the concept of the standard deviation in attempting to classify crop regions. The result is a system of regional classification where it is possible for the variance within regions to be significantly greater than the variance between regions.

Of course, many geographers have been able to use statistical methods for regional analysis without making fundamental errors. For several years Zobler [126] has been using the chi-square test to analyze regions, although some of his procedures have been questioned also.

Of all the branches of statistical methodology, geographers have used correlation analysis most often and for the longest time. This dates back thirty years to Rose's [78, 79] mapping of coefficients of correlation between temperature and corn yield in the United States Corn Belt. Rose's interest in quantitative analysis of geographic data, at a time when very few geographers shared this interest, is further illustrated by the fact that, in 1936, he held a Post-Doctoral Social Science Research Fellowship to study "Statistical Theory and Methods as an Aid in Geographic Research". These studies attracted the attention of some statisticians and precipitated a discussion of the problem of lack of independence among areal observations.[4] Recently many geographers have become interested in the possibilities of areal correlation analysis. Two of the leaders in this field, McCarty and Robinson, have paid particular attention to the problem of the size of the areal units employed in the gathering of discrete geographical observations.[5]

One branch of statistics that is just beginning to receive attention in geography is sampling procedures.[6] With the continually increasing number of detailed, microscopic land use and agricultural location surveys, research in this field probably will continue to expand.

With geographic applications of statistical methods becoming so numerous it was inevitable that a geographer would write an elementary text in statistics for geographers. This task was performed a few years ago by Peguy [72], and more recently by Gregory [42]. Both of these books constitute excellent examples of the general failure of "statistical geography". While many of the previously mentioned efforts have provided insights toward the solution of certain specific problems there is still no quantitative, analytical framework for the study of what should be one of the basic concerns of geography — the areal distribution of phenomena. Peguy and Gregory have used only geographic data which can be described by linear frequency distributions and then used elementary linear methods to analyze these distributions.

Bivariate Statistical Theory

The mathematical statisticians have actually come much closer to providing this framework than the geographers. A mathematical statistician treats an areal

---

[4]See especially Neprash [71].

[5]McCarty [66], Robinson [76], Robinson and Bryson [77].

[6]See Blaut [10], Wood [121].

distribution as merely one example of a bivariate distribution with the two variables being independent of each other. Thus, the voluminous literature on Bivariate Statistical Theory is applicable to geography, and models such as the Bivariate Normal Distribution and the T^2 Distribution are useful tools for the statistical analysis of areal distributions.

This leads to an obvious question—why haven't geographers used these tools to analyze areal distributions? The most important reason is that the vast majority of geographers have been either unable or unwilling to understand and apply the complicated mathematical concepts of Bivariate Statistical Theory. Even the so-called "introductory" texts in this field require the reader to have an extensive knowledge of calculus, matrix algebra, and set theory.[7] Pitifully few geographers in the past have met these qualifications. The difficulty is intensified by the fact that a large proportion of the available literature is written for "n" not-necessarily-independent variables, making the methods difficult to apply, even when understood. With increasing emphasis on mathematics and the physical sciences in American education it is hoped that future generations of geographers will not have this problem.

There are two additional, and more fundamental, reasons why bivariate statistical methods are not altogether satisfactory for the analysis of areal distributions. One involves the choice of an arbitrary pair of orthogonal axes and the other deals with the representation of a spherical surface as a plane. These will be discussed in more detail in the next chapter. However, there are several tools of bivariate statistics that are invariant with respect to all co-ordinate systems and the inaccuracies due to the sphericity of the earth are negligible when even moderately large areas are being studied. Therefore, much of bivariate statistical theory can be useful in analyzing areal distributions. In fact, much of the recent literature in mathematical statistics has been devoted to the accuracy of weapons, emphasizing the analysis of the areal·distribution of shots (usually guided missiles) at a target.

There are also many articles not related to weapons testing that are applicable to the analysis of areal distributions. Among the most useful of these are Haldane's [44] comments on the median, Hsu's [50, 51] studies of sampling from a bivariate normal population, and Villars and Anderson's [109] work on inference for bivariate normal distributions.

Location Theory and Regional Science

Economists, sociologists, ecologists and other persons whose primary interests are outside of the fields of geography and statistics have, nevertheless, played a leading role in the development of techniques of areal analysis. Theories dealing with the location of economic resources are the modern descendants of von Thünen's [103] theory of agricultural location patterns. The heart of this theory was a description of the probable areal arrangement of land use, agricultural intensity, rents, etc. around the one central city of an isolated state. Although changes in patterns of settlement and methods of agriculture, industry, and transportation have made many of the details of von Thünen's argument no longer valid, major components of this theory are still very much in use today.[8]

---

[7]An example is Anderson [3]. This volume also contains an extensive bibliography on pp. 356-368.

[8]For a discussion of the current usefulness of von Thünen's theories see Grotewold [43].

Large cities and metropolitan areas are often treated as isolated states and areal patterns of concentric circles are used to analyze the economic and social structure within these urban areas.

Several economists since von Thünen have been principally concerned with location. Of course, the emphasis has shifted from agricultural to industrial locations as the factory has become the dominant form of economic organization. Some of the leading contributors to Location Theory have been Weber [35], Christaller [16], and Lösch [62] in Germany; Ponsard [74] in France; and Hoover [49] and Isard [52] in the United States.

One of the most encouraging recent trends has been the increasing number of geographers and statisticians who have become concerned with the location of economic activity. A pioneer in this development has been Walter Isard who, in addition to being the most prolific writer in the field, combined his interests in the study of economic theory, econometrics, and geography (particularly regional analysis) and formed the Regional Science Association and the Department of Regional Science at the University of Pennsylvania. Somehow, Professor Isard [53] has also found time to write an extensive book on regional analysis. In addition to the content, an outstanding feature of this volume is the huge bibliography of papers relating to Location Theory and Regional Science.

One corollary to Location Theory has been the study of the distribution of urban centers. Central Place Theory was formally developed by Christaller [16] and many of the recent studies have been conducted by Garrison and Berry, while they were at the University of Washington.[9] Other Americans and several Swedes have also been active in this field.

The analysis of the spacing of individuals of a population, originally used in the physical sciences, has been further developed recently by plant ecologists.[10] These investigations have led to the use of nearest neighbor distances as measures of areal dispersion, and to the development of methods for testing the degree of randomness in an areal distribution.[11] Previously, geographers had used similar concepts to study spacing in sparsely populated areas.[12] These methods will be discussed in more detail in Chapter VII.

Social Physics and Macrogeography

Henry C. Carey, the most famous of the early American economists, was probably the first man to both recognize and quantify the effects of number of people and distance on economic, social, and political events. He wrote that:

> "Man, the molecule of society, is the subject of Social Science. . . . The great law of *Molecular Gravitation* [is] the indispensable condition of the existence of the being known as man. . . . The greater the number collected in a given space, the greater is the attractive force that is there exerted. . . . Gravitation is here, as everywhere, in the *direct* ratio of the mass, and the *inverse* one of distance."[13]

[9]Beckman [7], Berry and Garrison [8, 9], Brush [12].

[10]Viktorov [108], Goodall 40 .

[11]Dice [26], Skellam [83], Clark and Evans [18, 19], Morisita [69], Thompson [102], Dacey [23, 24, 25].

[12]Barnes and Robinson [6], Mather [65].

[13]Carey, *Principles of Social Science* (Philadelphia: J. B. Lippincott and Co., 1858-1859) as quoted in Carrothers [14]. p. 94.

Carey suggested that this formula accounted for land values and predicted, on the basis of the "law", that the distance factor would eventually help to end British domination of India. He saw great advantages of mutual association and believed that increasing population densities would benefit mankind. Thus, Carey was not only concerned with interrelationships among economics, geography, and statistics, he brought sociology, political science, philosophy, and even physics and astronomy into the same general system.

Of course, the concept of the unity of knowledge or even a unified social science did not originate with Carey. Leibniz was actively opposing the Newton-inspired increase in specialization among scholars in the seventeenth century. Adolphe Quetelet, a famous statistician and astronomer, wrote his book on "Social Physics" in 1836 in which he observed that "It seems to be that that which relates to the human species, considered *en masse*, is of the order of physical facts; the greater the number of individuals the more the individual will be effaced. . . ."[14]

The major difficulty in these efforts was that the early practitioners of social physics were overly enthusiastic. The most fundamental change in this field has occurred with the substitution of a quest for empirical statistical regularities and overall patterns rather than Quetelet's perfect natural law. However, many of the basic principles remain—the most important contributions of social physicists are still the applications of Carey's gravity model.

A large proportion of the recent research in this field has been conducted as part of the Social Physics Project at Princeton University, under the leadership of John Q. Stewart, Professor Emeritus of Astronomical Physics. The relevance of social physics to the study of areal distributions can be seen by examining Stewart's ([92], pp. 19-20) definition of the subject. "Social physics analyzes sociological situations in terms of physical factors. Fundamental physical factors are time, distance, and numbers of people . . . ." Obviously, any system in which distance is a primary factor is very closely related to the study of areal distributions.

The investigation of the role of distance in social science is the objective of the Macrogeography Project at the American Geographical Society, under the direction of William Warntz, who was one of Stewart's associates at Princeton. Warntz ([112], pp. 449-450) has provided a rather complete definition of the aims and scope of the macrogeographical aspects of social physics.

> "At the American Geographical Society, emphasis has been upon the investigation of distance as one of the basic dimensions of society. There have been a great number of appropriate statistical testings of working hypotheses which not only have proved to be important at the empirical inductive level but also have occasioned a generalized deductive approach.

> An examination of the underlying considerations and general results of these projects suggests that knowledge of a broad general nature in the social sciences can be won only

---

[14]Quetelet, *Sur l'homme* (Brussels: Louis Hauman and Co., 1836) as quoted in Stewart [93], p. 243.

if the true dimensions of the subject are analyzed. Hence, there is a search for irreducible primitive dimensions and the realization that time, distance, number of people, and a few other dimensions are the basic categories upon which the structures of theory can be built. Physical distance, like time, is no less important a dimension in the analysis of social phenomena than it is for physical phenomena. It is with this dimension that the macrogeographer is basically concerned; it is the *sine qua non* of macrogeography.

The adoption of the macroscopic point of view is of course vital to these studies. Currently, microgeography as the study of small areas, and macrogeography as the study of large areas, are generally accepted definitions. In physics, however, macroscopic refers to the manifestations of the aggregate effects of the combined microscopic units. . . . It is the purpose of one of the projects at the American Geographical Society and the Social Physics Project to undertake macroscopic analysis in the same sense as in physics. In geography, very small area studies are necessarily microscopic, but the assembly of more and more area studies involving an increase in the quantity of detail does not mean *per se* a shift from the microscopic to the macroscopic.

. . . It is the contention in this macroscopic approach that the forging of a theory of human society can be greatly aided by finding regularities in the aggregate. . . . In social science, as in physical science the behavior of the individual may not be considered as determined, but in both sciences aggregate behavior viewed macroscopically is determined and generalizations about it can be made, once the proper dimensions are isolated and recognized."

Much of the work at Princeton and the American Geographical Society consists of wider application and further refinement of Carey's "gravitational" principle of the influence of people at a distance (called "potential of population" by Stewart).[15] Other researchers, notably Dodd and Zipf, have used the gravity model to analyze flows of people and transactions between two areas.[16] Recently, Stewart and Warntz [96] have used these methods to investigate the distribtuion of density of population in both rural and urban areas.

In general, the social physicists have made two major contributions to the study of areal distributions. The first is the demonstration of the socio-economic significance of some of the statistical measures that will be discussed in Chapters IV and V. The adoption of the macroscopic point of view is the other great contribution of the social physicists. Areal relationships among aggregates can provide insights which may never be seen by a microscopic analysis of the individual members of a population.

[15]Stewart [86, 88, 89, 90, 91, 92, 93], Stewart and Warntz [95, 97], Warntz [114, 115, 116, 118], Neft [70].

[16]Cavanaugh [15], Carrothers [14], Dodd [28, 29], Zipf [124], pp. 347-444 and [125].

Centrography

The study of various types of "centers" of areal distributions began in the United States in the 1870's. Shortly thereafter, the great Russian chemist D. I. Mendeleev [67] began investigating the "center of gravity" of Russia. Several of his countrymen, led by E. E. Sviatlovsky, took up this idea of "centrography" and formed the Mendeleev Centrographical Laboratory in Leningrad in 1925. However, no area can be analyzed solely in terms of centers; this should merely be one part of an integrated system of analysis for areal distributions. In particular the centrographers failed to consider the possible significance of areal dispersion. However, this was ignored in the 1920's and 1930's when there was an international "race", led by the Americans, Russians, and Italians, to see who could compute the most centers.[17]

By the late 1930's centrography had fallen into disfavor because it couldn't live up to the absurd claims of some of its proponents, particularly in the Soviet Union,[18] and because it had proved to be virtually useless as an isolated discipline. When this happened, the positive contributions of the centrographers also disappeared from geographical and statistical literature.

Of course, centrography was never really an independent discipline. The methods used were simply straightforward applications of bivariate statistical theory. However, it was an organized attempt to introduce quantitative methods into the study of areal distributions.

A few papers dealing with matters related to this field have appeared recently. Hart [46] , in his discussion of centrography, succeeded mainly in reintroducing errors regarding the concept of an areal median which had been corrected a generation earlier. Bachi [5] has made an important contribution by using a measure of dispersion to supplement the centers. Another recent effort is a monograph called *Statistical Geography* written by three sociologists, Duncan, Cuzzort, and Duncan [30]. While this volume contains adequate summaries of the methods of Bachi, Robinson, and others, almost no new ideas, concepts, or methods are introduced. This book serves to emphasize that no one has ever established a fairly complete, internally consistent, useful system of statistical analysis for areal distributions.

17The best bibliographies and summaries of these studies are included in Sviatlovsky and Eells [99] and Gini, Boldrini, Galvani, and Venere [38].

18An excellent brief account of the demise of Soviet centrography appears in Poulsen [75].

CHAPTER II
AREAL DISTRIBUTIONS

The place of quantitative methods in geography is currently the subject of much discussion and debate within that profession. It is the stated contention here that statistical methodology is absolutely necessary, although not sufficient, for progress in geography. Of course, the validity and usefulness of each particular method that is proposed must be adequately demonstrated. But the desirability of quantitative methods for geographic research can no longer be seriously questioned. If this position is accepted, the next task is to define the specific scope and purpose of this study.

Two-Dimensional Areal Distributions

The terms areal distribution, geographical distribution, and spatial distribution often are used interchangeably. In this study an areal distribution will mean phenomena distributed over a portion of the surface area of a celestial body. This will usually be the earth although the distribution of craters on the moon or the "canals" on Mars are perfectly acceptable examples of areal distributions. Geographical distributions are all those that have application in geography including many linear distributions such as the arrangement of phenomena along railroad lines, highways, rivers, etc. There are also many linear distributions that are basically transformations of areal data. As an illustration, consider the distribution of the number of pupils living within specified distances of the school they attend. Although the original data could be presented in the form of an areal distribution, the actual presentation is merely an ordinary linear distribution since the variable dealing with direction has been removed from the data.

A spatial distribution exists when the base includes area plus the dimension of height above or below the surface. Thus, the cloud patterns at a given instant in time could be studied as a spatial distribution with the location and height of the clouds serving as the base and the size or moisture content as the characteristic variable to be analyzed.

The purpose of this work is to propose a simple, integrated system of statistical analysis for areal distributions. In no sense is this intended to be a complete study of statistical geography. Duncan ([30], p. 19) defines four " 'perspectives on areal differentiation'; (a) chorographic interest in areal differentiation, i.e., in the characteristics of areas; (b) interest in areal distribution; (c) interest in spatial structure; and (d) concern with the explanation of areal variation. To these 'perspectives' must be added (e) the use of areal data for objectives not intrinsically related to areal differentiation or spatial pattern." Using this framework, the primary concern here will be (b). Since (a) and (d) are very closely related to (b), much of this study will be applicable to these perspectives.

The system of analysis to be employed in this study is based on the application of some of the fundamental concepts of statistics to areal distributions.

The first of these is the concept of a deviation, which in general may be considered as the difference between any two values of a variable, expressed in the same units as the values of the variable.

> "But, one can also think of a deviation as a length or distance between positions on the mathematical line representing the values of the variable over which the population is distributed. This idea is easily transferred to distributions over actual physical areas. . . . . Here, a deviation may be thought of as the physical distance between the position of a unit of the population and another specified point, with the distance expressed in some convenient units of physical length such as miles.[1]"

This definition produces a "two-dimensional" areal distribution where the areal base is represented by one dimension, distance, rather than by a two-dimensional coordinate system such as latitude and longitude. As mentioned previously the two-dimensional approach has three advantages over the three-dimensional system that is treated within the framework of bivariate statistical theory. One is that the reduction in variables makes this system easier to use. A more important advantage concerns the establishment of a coordinate system. Such a system is based on the construction of two orthogonal axes and deviations are defined as distances along these axes.

For example, assume that *Figure 1* represents a part of the earth's surface and a pair of orthogonal axes X and Y have been established. In the three-dimensional approach the distance between points A and B would have two components, x and y. In the system being used here the distance between these two points would be r. The relationship among the sides of such a right triangle is defined by the Pythagorean Theorem, $x^2 + y^2 = r^2$. Thus, for measures involving the second power of distance, the choice of coordinate system does not affect the value of such parameters.

However, if any other powers of distance are employed every pair of axes will lead to slightly different values for any given measure.[2] It is obviously undesirable to have parameters that are influenced by arbitrary decisions of the investigator. The two-dimensional approach eliminates this difficulty by simply removing the coordinate system and measuring distances directly.

It must be remembered that any map, *Figure 1* included, is merely the representation of area on a plane surface. Actually the earth is approximately an oblate spheroid, although, for the purposes of this study, the assumption of a sphere will be sufficiently accurate. Thus, the deviations that are to be considered are great circle distances on a sphere and not distances on a plane. The equation relating the sides of a right spherical triangle is not the familiar $r^2 = x^2 + y^2$ but, rather $cos\ r = cos\ x\ \ cos\ y$. Therefore, even when squared distances are used, the two systems do not give the same result since r never actually equals $(x^2 + y^2)^{1/2}$.

Of course, when the distances involved are not too large these differences are extremely small. But when these distances are greater than one-tenth the

---

[1]Warntz and Neft [119], pp. 47-48.

[2]For a further discussion of this problem see pp. 30-33.

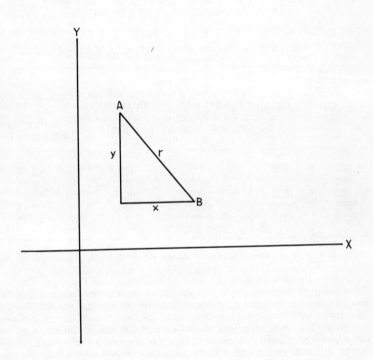

FIGURE 1.—Plane Right Triangle

circumference of the sphere, the differences become very significant. In the case of a spherical right equilateral triangle, the ratio of the actual r to the r calculated using the Pythagorean Theorem for plane right triangles is $1 : \sqrt{2}$. For distances greater than one-fourth of the circumference of the sphere, this ratio decreases very rapidly and the use of a bivariate coordinate system becomes absurd. The effect of the sphericity of the earth for five hypothetical examples is illustrated in *Table 1*.

TABLE 1.

THE EFFECT OF THE SPHERICITY OF THE EARTH
ON THE CALCULATION OF DISTANCES

Mean Circumference of the Earth = 24,874 miles*				
x (miles)	y (miles)	$r_1 = \sqrt{x^2 + y^2}$ (miles)	r_2 where $\cos r_2$ $= \cos x \cos y$ (miles)	$\dfrac{r_1 - r_2}{r_2} \times 100$ (percentage difference in r)
300	400	500	499.7	0.06
400	2300	2335	2331	0.17
800	1500	1700	1691	0.53
3000	4000	5000	4649	7.75
6218.5	6218.5	$x \sqrt{2} = 8794.3$	6218.5	41.42

*Calculated from measurements given in Woodward [122], pp. xliii-liii.

Once again it must be stated that the three-dimensional approach does have certain advantages in some situations. When the area being studied is not large and measures involving squared distances are being used, the great amount of literature dealing with bivariate statistics and the use of familiar terminology in that literature constitutes an advantage for the use of that system. However, this study will deal exclusively with the two-dimensional approach to the analysis of *any* areal distribution.

Areal Frequency Distributions

One of the basic operations of linear statistics is the condensation of a great number of observations into the orderly form of a frequency distribution. "Frequency" in this case means the number of units of the population falling within a particular "class". The classes are specified distance intervals along the mathematical line that forms the base of the distribution. The use of the word "frequency" in this connection is not altogether satisfactory because, in science, frequency usually has a relation to time. However, since this usage of frequency has been universally accepted, it will be used here, although "class-density" might be a better term.[3] From this, it is easy to conceive of "linear density of population" as the number of items of the population in a unit of length. For areal distributions, the class is a segment of area and frequency becomes the number of units of the population falling within a specified area. The familiar "areal density of population" is, therefore, defined as the number of members of a population in a unit of area. Thus, one can think of a common map of population density as an areal frequency distribution.

These applications of the concepts of deviation and frequency form the basis of the whole system of statistical analysis for areal distributions. From the definition of deviation a system of parameters and procedures of estimation and inference will be constructed to describe areal distributions. Densities will be used to permit the orderly presentation and computational advantages associated with "grouped" data and to construct certain models of areal distribution.

The actual construction of an areal frequency distribution from raw data presents several problems. Chief among these, and common to both areal and linear statistics, is the selection of an appropriate number of classes. Unfortunately, the two factors influencing this decision pull in opposite directions. The best presentation is achieved when there is a regular pattern of frequencies so that the distribution can be easily described by a "smoothed" density curve or surface. This usually requires a relatively small number of classes.

However, data organized in this form are often used to compute measures describing the distribution. Since each item now takes some central value of the class instead of its observed value, the accuracy of the results will vary directly with the number of classes.

In practice, this problem is more complex in the areal case than it is for linear distributions. The added dimension of area is itself a complication which is accentuated by the fact that many actual areal distributions are quite irregular and difficult to describe by a smoothed density surface.

Statistics texts contain many formulas and "rule of thumb" suggestions for the selection of the number of classes. However, for areal distributions, common sense and a little experience will serve better than any formula. Usage is the significant factor--use a large number of classes when they are to serve as the basis for extensive calculations and employ a smaller number of classes when the presentation of a smoothed surface is the primary object. One guide to this decision can be "borrowed" from linear statistics. Croxton and Cowden ([21], p. 160) have suggested that most frequency distributions should have between 6 and 16 classes. For areal distributions, these numbers have to be squared, but since most areas are not squares the resulting figures should be reduced. Experience with hundreds of distributions as part of the American Geographical Society's Macrogeography Project has shown that most areal frequency distributions should have between 20 and 125 classes. Detailed analysis of an extremely large area (e.g., the earth) may require as many as 500 classes.

---

[3]This would be a density in the sense that it is the number of items per class area. However, "class-density" is not a completely satisfactory term since density usually refers to the number of items per unit area. Classes cannot always be considered to be analagous to unit areas. For example, all the classes of a given distribution may not have the same area.

Almost all linear frequency distributions are constructed with equal class intervals. This is done to permit easy comparability among the various classes. While equal area and shape of areal classes also are desirable, these rarely can be obtained. This is caused by the fact that the so-called "raw data" are usually already in the form of an areal frequency distribution with administrative divisions serving as the classes (e.g., population by county, wheat production by state, etc.). The comparability among classes is limited, but by no means destroyed, by this condition.[4]

In linear statistics, the mid-value of the class is used as the value for all the items in that class. For areal distributions, all the members of a class are assumed to be located at one "control point". This may be one of the measures of average position discussed in Chapter IV or an arbitrarily selected location which combines some of the properties of a few of these "centers". Once again, usage is the factor which should determine the appropriate choice of control point in any particular case.

As an illustration of the construction of an areal frequency distribution, *Figure 2* shows the 99 classes and control points that were used to analyze the 1960 population of the United States.

Populations and Samples

One of the difficulties encountered in discussing statistics and geography is the double meaning of the word "population". In this work, the term sometimes will be used, as it was in the preceding paragraph, to mean the number of human beings. However, most of the time the word will be used in the statistical sense, as synonymous with the logical term "universe". In this case population refers to a collection of discrete items. These items may be human beings, non-human aggregates such as dollars of income, number of cattle, or barrels of petroleum, or events such as business failures.

With the exception of this ambiguity, the ordinary definitions of statistical processes apply here. A *sample* is a part of a population and a measure derived from a sample is a *statistic*. A *parameter* is a measure describing an attribute of a population.

These definitions provide the basis for the establishment of a system of symbols and notation. In general, the Latin alphabet will be used, with parameters being denoted by capital letters, and statistics by small letters. Internal consistency and facility were the objectives but, wherever feasible, symbols were chosen that would demonstrate the relationship between certain areal measures and their linear counterparts. Individual symbols will be discussed as the measures are introduced and a complete list appears as *Appendix A*.

---

[4]Croxton and Cowden [21], pp. 164-166.

FIGURE 2. —The 99 Classes and Control Points Used in the Analysis of the Areal Distribution of the Population of the United States in 1960

CHAPTER III
MOMENTS

Physical and Statistical Moments

The concept of "moments" was used initially in the physical sciences. In mechanics the term usually refers to the measure of a force with reference to its tendency to produce rotation. This "moment of force" or "torque" is defined as "the product of a force F times the perpendicular distance between its line of application and the axis of rotation d".[1] Thus, L (torque) = Fd. The physicists generalized this principle to define a "first moment of area" with respect to an axis of rotation as $\int_A s \cdot dA$ where s is the perpendicular distance from the reference axis to the element of area dA. The next step in the process of generalization was the construction of a system of moments based on these definitions. Thus, $\int_A s^2 \cdot dA$ became the "second moment of area" or the "moment of inertia of the area", and the "n^{th} moment of area" was defined as $\int_A s^n \cdot dA$.

In statistics, this concept has been applied to the analysis of frequency distributions. Since the mid-values of the classes represent a discrete, rather than continuous, distribution a process of mechanical integration must be used. The "n^{th} statistical moment" about a point is defined as $\dfrac{\sum f(d^n)}{N}$. In this case f is the class frequency which is the statistical term that corresponds to force in mechanics. Distance d means the deviation between the given point and all the class mid-values. The only basic difference between the physical and statistical definitions is that physical moments are aggregate measures while statistical moments are average measures since the product numerator is divided by the total number of observations in the frequency distribution N.

The use of this concept in linear statistics has been summarized by Mills ([68], p. 168):

> "These moments constitute sensitive measures of the attributes of frequency distributions. In particular, the degree and character of variation are defined by these moments with great accuracy. Slight differences in patterns of variation are reflected in the moments. These moments yield, moreover, the basic descriptive measures already discussed [arithmetic mean and standard deviation], and other highly serviceable measures."

In fact, the use of the first four moments provides the most efficient means for describing the characteristics of any linear frequency distribution. Moments are also used extensively as a basis for describing a sample distribution by a

---

Margenau, Watson and Montgomery [64], p. 30.

mathematical model. This "method of moments" is usually identified with the system of 12 model frequency curves developed by Karl Pearson.[2] Statistical moments continue to be of great value when areal, rather than linear, distributions are to be described and analyzed.

Areal Moments

Areal moments are similar in form to ordinary statistical moments except for the fact that areal moments are not based on reference lines or axes. However, the basic characteristic of moments is retained: the number of the moment is equal to the exponent of distance that is used. Thus the value of the nth *areal moment*, M'_n, at a point j is defined as $\frac{1}{P}\int_A r^n \cdot dA$ where P represents the number of items in the population and r is the great circle distance[3] between j and the element of area dA. In practice, areal populations are finite and discrete and a process of mechanical integration replaces the above formula. Thus,

$$M'_n \text{ at } j = \frac{\sum\limits_{x=1}^{P} r_{jx}^n}{P}$$

where r_{jx} is the distance between j and the location of a member of the population, x. When areal frequency distributions are used

$$M'_n \text{ at } j = \frac{\sum\limits_{i=1}^{N} (p_i r_{ij}^n)}{P}.$$

In this formula i represents a class, N is the number of classes in the distribution, p_i is the number of items (frequency) of class i, and r_{ij} is the distance between j and the control point of class i.

Since j can be any one of the infinite number of points comprising an area, these moments are areally continuous variables. This is true despite the fact that the moments are derived from a population which consists of a finite number of discrete individuals. If values of an areal moment are computed for a large number of points, a map of the area can be drawn showing iso-lines connecting points of equal value. In this way, the concept of moments can be used to increase the level of abstraction in the study of areal distributions. The calculation of a moment distribution transforms a microgeographic collection of individual items into a macrogeographic, areally continuous variable.

This system of moments serves as the basis for most of the measures to be developed in this study. The remainder of this chapter will be devoted to a brief discussion of the general properties of this system, while the detailed characteristics of each moment will be described in later chapters.

[2]See Elderton [32].

[3]When discussing areal distributions, distance between any two positions will henceforth always mean the shortest great circle distance on the surface of a sphere from one of these points to the other, although this will no longer be stated explicitly every time the word "distance" is used.

Properties of Areal Moments

The most important distinction between ordinary statistical moments and areal moments is that areal moments can never have negative values. This results from the definition of distance used in this study which treats all distances as positive deviations. This means that the odd-numbered areal moments have different characteristics than their counterparts in linear statistics. For example, the third areal moment cannot be used to indicate the degree of symmetry of an areal distribution.

Statistical moments can be used to construct an integrated system of measures of central tendency and dispersion. Areal moments can serve a similar function. A measure of central tendency of an areal distribution is a location, a specific point on an area, and will be called a *measure of average position*. The location of the minimum value of the nth root of M'_n ($\sqrt[n]{M'_n}$) represents such a measure.[4] Thus, a measure of average position could be defined for each one of the infinite number of possible values of n. However, only small integers are commonly employed as values of n since extreme locations have an overwhelming influence on the higher numbered moments.

This situation has been very well explained for linear statistics by Crum and Patton ([22], p. 217) and their argument also is applicable to the areal case:

> "Even for the first moment an extremely large or small value of the variate has undue influence on the result. For the second moment this extreme variate has a much greater relative effect because of the squaring process: the extreme deviation is weighted by a large number, that deviation itself, whereas a moderate deviation is weighted by a small number, the moderate deviation. As moments of higher order involve raising the deviations to higher powers, it is evident that a single extreme variate may dominate the values of the higher moments, and quite out-weigh the other *N-1* variates. . . . In most cases encountered in practice there are some extreme variates, and, although there may be no single very exceptional variate, moments above the fourth are likely to be quite unreliable.

This is one of the reasons why low order *inverse areal moments* (particularly $n=-1$) are frequently used, since extreme locations exert very little influence on their value and, therefore, on the location of their minimum value.

Measures of average position based on inverse areal moments have two additional properties that are not true when n is greater than zero. The first is that such measures of average position *must* be located within the area being

---

[4]In practice it is not necessary to compute values of $\sqrt[n]{M_n}$ in order to locate average positions. When $n>0$ the measures of average position will be located at the minimum value of M'_n. When $n<0$, the measures will be located at the maximum value of M'_n. The formula using $\sqrt[n]{M_n}$ serves to combine these two conditions into one expression and to relate this to the formula for measures of dispersion which soon will be discussed.

considered. Secondly, this location must be in a region where the density of the population being studied is very large in relation to the density over the rest of the area. Measures based on positive areal moments may possess these characteristics but they do not have to have them. This is analagous to the situation in linear statistics where the mean and the median (related to positive statistical moments) are good centers only for distributions of the normal type. "In the case of a U-shaped distribution, the mean is likely to indicate where the *fewest* values are and is meaningless for most practical purposes."[5] Since irregular, extremely asymmetrical and multi-modal areal distributions are the rule rather than the exception, this becomes a major factor in the selection of an appropriate measure of average position to describe an areal population.

Areal moments can also be used to indicate the dispersion of an areal population. Such measures are defined by the magnitude of the minimum value of $\sqrt[n]{M_n'}$. It is evident that all such measures are in units of physical distance r. This feature permits more valid comparisons among measures of areal dispersion than among their linear counterparts which are likely to be in different units.

The magnitude of these measures of areal dispersion for a given population must be in the order of the moments on which they are based— *min.* $\sqrt[n]{M_n'}$ varies directly with the value of n. An investigator's choice of an appropriate measure will largely depend on three factors: how heavily he wishes his results to be influenced by extreme locations, about which measure of average position he wishes to calculate the dispersion, and the effects on his data of certain biases and sources of inaccuracy associated with these measures. This last factor will be discussed in the following sections of this chapter and in subsequent parts of this work. In addition, a fourth criterion must be mentioned although it has nothing to do with the characteristics of the measures themselves. An investigator will often compute the value of a particular parameter in order to compare the result with similar measures presented in previously published studies.

One feature of areal moments that now is apparent is the tremendous importance of the minimum value of $\sqrt[n]{M_n'}$. This one value for any areal moment defines the two basic statistical parameters—the measures of average position and dispersion.

Besides these direct uses, areal moments will be employed in expressions to indicate other characteristics of areal populations. Included among these will be measures of relative dispersion, generalized dispersion, skewness, and kurtosis. Some of these simply will be ratios of two moments while others will include terms other than moments.

In linear statistics some values of moments have to be corrected for systematic errors of grouping. This is necessary because all the observations

---

[5]Ferber [34], p. 24.

in a class of a frequency distribution are assumed to be concentrated at the midpoint of that class. If the distribution is close to the normal type, more than half of the observations in a class will lie between the midpoint and the class boundary that is nearer the peak of the distribution. For even numbered moments, where there are no negative terms, this results in a systematic error where the computed value is greater than the actual value of the moment. The most commonly used correction for this error was proposed by Sheppard [82] before the turn of the century. This modification is applicable when three conditions prevail:

1. When there are a large number of observations (usually stated as at least 500).

2. When the data are observations on a continuous variable.

3. When the frequency curve of the distribution asymptotically approaches the x-axis at both tails. This condition is often described as the curve having "high contact".

A similar set of correction formulas could be developed for areal moments. Such a system would seem to be even more useful in the areal case since the systematic error affects all areal moments because there can never be negative deviations. However, there are four reasons why such a system, if developed, could almost never be used:

1. Areal data in the form of continuous areal variables are rare. This is particularly true in the social sciences where continuous distributions (i.e., areal moments) usually must be derived from discrete data. Several continuous areal variables do exist in the physical sciences with data relating to such subjects as magnetism and atmospheric pressure.

2. Few of the continuous areal distributions that do exist are of the normal type with high contact in all directions.

3. The control point of an areal class is not usually assumed to be at the "center" of the area of that class. The location of the control point should be influenced by the distribution of population within the class. Thus, when dealing with areal distributions the selection of control points becomes the major "correction factor". If this is done intelligently the systematic grouping error in areal moments will be minor.

4. A formal system of correction factors, such as Sheppard's, is based on equal size of class intervals. In many cases, data for areal frequency distributions can be obtained only for classes with unequal areas.

There is also another source of systematic error due to grouping that affects M'_n when n is positive. This can be shown using the simple linear illustration in *Figure 3(a)*. Two members of the population are located at x_1 and

24

a)

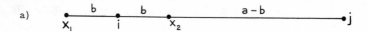

b)

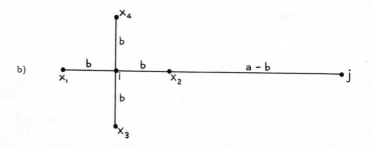

FIGURE 3. —Hypothetical Distribution to Illustrate the Effect of Systematic
Grouping Errors on the Calculation of Areal Moments

x_2. M_n' at $j = \dfrac{\sum\limits_{x=1}^{2} r_{jx}^n}{2} = \dfrac{(a+b)^n + (a-b)^n}{2}$. Now consider the case of an areal

frequency distribution where x_1 and x_2 are the only members of a class and the control point of that class is assumed to be at i, surely a most reasonable lo-

cation. In this case M_n' at $j = \dfrac{\sum\limits_{i=1}^{1} (2r_{ij}^n)}{2} = a^n$. When $n \geq 2$, $\left[(a+b)^n + (a-b)^n\right]/2 > a^n$.

Thus, the use of grouped data has resulted in an understatement of the value of some of the areal moments. When $n=1$, $\left[(a+b)+(a-b)\right]/2 = a$ and there is no error.

The magnitude of this error is increased when all the observations in the class are not on the line connecting i and j. *Figure 3(b)* is a simple example of this case. To facilitate calculation and presentation, only the second moment will be used in this illustration,[6] but the effect also applies to all positive areal

moments, including M_1'. M_2' at $j = \dfrac{\sum\limits_{x=1}^{4} r_{jx}^2}{4} = \dfrac{(a+b)^2 + (a-b)^2 + \left(\sqrt{a^2+b^2}\right)^2 + \left(\sqrt{a^2+b^2}\right)^2}{4} =$

$a^2 + b^2$. When x_1, x_2, x_3, x_4 are assumed to be grouped at i, M_2' at $j =$

$\dfrac{\sum\limits_{i=1}^{1} (4r_{ij}^2)}{4} = a^2$. Since $a^2 + b^2 > a^2$, the bias toward understatement due to

grouping is apparent. Fortunately, the need for drastic measures to correct this effect is reduced by the fact that this source of error moves in a direction opposite to the one mentioned previously, with the result that the two sources of error display some tendency to counteract each other. In practice, the easiest way to increase the accuracy of positive areal moments is to increase the number of classes. Using the symbols of *Figure 3*, this would reduce the value

of $\dfrac{b}{a}$. For a given areal distribution, if the maximum b is less than one-tenth

of the average a the resulting calculations of areal moments will be very accurate.

This condition leads to a valuable rule concerning the limits of the magnitudes of positive areal moments. Let us assume that an entire population is located at

point i. Then M_n' at point $j = \dfrac{\sum\limits_{i=1}^{1} (Pr_{ij}^n)}{P} = r_{ij}^n$ and the minimum value of

$\sqrt[n]{M_n'}$ is located at i. Any change in the location of the members of the

---

[6]This bias is demonstrated for all positive moments in *Appendix B*.

population without changing the location of the minimum value of $\sqrt[n]{M_n'}$ cannot result in a decrease in the magnitude of M_n' at j for any $n > 0$. This means that the value of a positive areal moment at a given point must be greater than or equal to the distance from that point to the measure of average position based on that moment (M_n' at $j \overset{\geq}{=} r_{cj}^n$ where c is the location of the minimum value of $\sqrt[n]{M_n'}$ and $n > 0$).

The preceding has been a discussion of the general properties of the system of areal moments. The characteristics of specific moments and their related measures of average position and dispersion will be treated in the following two chapters. Additional measures, not based on moments also will be developed in these sections.

CHAPTER IV
MEASURE OF AVERAGE POSITIONS

A measure of central tendency in statistics is usually defined as a single value of a variable that is in some way functionally related to the value of each individual item in the distribution. However, such a parameter also could be described as a point or position on the horizontal axis or scale of values of the variable. The location of this point is in some way functionally related to the positions assignable to the items of the population as these items are distributed along this same mathematical line.

This makes it easy to think of a measure of central tendency for an areal distribution as some point or position that is functionally related to the locations of the members of the population as they are distributed over the area under consideration. Hence, the name *average position*.

Most of the measures that will be mentioned in this chapter are areal counterparts of linear concepts. An effort has been made to emphasize these relationships through the choice of names for the measures of average position. Thus, terms such as arithmetic mean, median, mode, harmonic mean, and geometric mean will appear frequently in this study.

The Arithmetic Mean Center

The *arithmetic mean center* (S_C) of an areal population is the location of the minimum value of $\sqrt{M_2'}$, or more simply, the position of the minimum value of M_2'. This is analogous to the concept of the arithmetic mean which also has the property that it represents the location of the minimum value of the sum of the squared deviations.

The arithmetic mean center has the longest history of any of the parameters used to describe areal distributions and also has been used more often than any of the other measures. It was first used in physics as the *center of gravity* of mass distributed over an area. The first application of this principle to human populations was made almost a century ago by Hilgard [48]. The Bureau of the Census started using this "center of population" in this first *Statistical Atlas of the United States*, compiled under the direction of Francis A. Walker [110], part II, pp. 5-6) and published in 1874.

The arithmetic mean centers computed by physicists and by statisticians of the Bureau of the Census were not located by finding the point at which the value of the second areal moment was a minimum. Since the second power of distance is involved, the Pythagorean Theorem is applicable, and the location of this center is invariant with respect to the choice of a coordinate system. Thus, virtually all arithmetic mean centers have been calculated as the point representing the arithmetic mean of the X values and the arithmetic mean of the Y values where X and Y were a pair of orthogonal axes.

When the great Russian chemist Mendeleev turned his attention to demography at the start of the twentieth century, he faced an additional problem in the calculation of the arithmetic mean center. The area of Russia was so vast that Mendeleev felt that he could not ignore the effect of the sphericity of the earth on the location of the center.[1] His son, then a student in mathematics at Petrograd University, became the first person to employ formulas treating the earth as a sphere in the calculation of the arithmetic mean center when he computed the center of gravity of the Russian population for 1897. However, these formulas are very complex and it is easier to find the location of the minimum value of the second areal moment than it is to modify the bivariate approach to account for the sphericity of the earth. The relationships among these various methods for computing and defining this center were clearly shown when Gini and Galvani [39] proved that the value of M'_2 is a minimum at S_C.

Most of the characteristics of the arithmetic mean center are true, to a greater or lesser extent, of all measures of average position based on positive areal moments. As such, these properties were outlined in Chapter III but, nevertheless, their importance warrants restatement here:

1. S_C does not have to be located inside the area under consideration. This can be easily demonstrated by using the "L" shaped area shown in *Figure 4*. Assuming a population consisting of x_1, x_2, x_3, x_4, and x_5, S_C is located as shown, outside the area.

2. S_C does not necessarily indicate any characteristics of the region where it is located. For example, the fact that the arithmetic mean center of the United States in 1960 was located near Centralia, Illinois does not reveal any information about demographic, economic, or sociological conditions near Centralia.

3. S_C is greatly affected by extreme locations.

4. S_C is extremely sensitive. *Any* movement within the population will cause some change in its location although the change may be minute.

This sensitivity to internal movements makes the arithmetic mean center a very useful parameter for studying general trends in the pattern of an areal distribution over a long period of time. However, the first three characteristics mentioned above severely limit the usefulness of S_C for most other purposes. It is not a very effective measure for the selection of optimum locations in an area or as a tool of regional analysis. The basic mistake of the centrographers was that they ignored these factors when they indiscriminately compared arithmetic mean centers of various areal distributions of socio-economic phenomena for a given region. They only succeeded in demonstrating that S_C alone cannot serve as a basis for socio-economic planning decisions.

The usefulness of S_C is not strictly limited to time series analysis. It may be used in conjunction with other parameters to compare areal patterns of a phenomenon for various regions. Also, the usefulness of S_C is increased by the centrographic "fever" of a generation ago. During that period of activity, several hundred arithmetic mean centers were computed, providing a great backlog of

---

[1]Mendeleev [67], pp. 124-142.

illustrations to which present studies may be compared. S_C is the only measure to be discussed in this work for which an extensive reservoir of previous applications exists.

Finally, S_C has the advantage of possessing most of the valuable statistical properties of the arithmetic mean. This is particularly important when sampling procedures are used. This subject will be treated in Chapter IX but it can be noted here that the arithmetic mean of a sample is a very efficient statistic and its sampling distribution closely approximates a standard mathematical model. These two factors make the arithmetic mean center a valuable measure when inference and estimation procedures are to be used.

The concept of the arithmetic mean center can be applied to an area itself just as easily as it is applied to a population distributed over that area. This *center of area*, A_C, is simply the center of gravity of a portion of the surface area of a sphere where the density is assumed to be uniform over the area. A_C has the same characteristics as S_C, including the property that A_C does not have to be in the area (see *Figure 4*).[2]

A rule can now be formulated which limits the location of some other measures of average position with respect to S_C and A_C. The location of the minimum value of $\sqrt{M'_n}$ where $n > 2$ must be closer to both A_C and S_C than S_C is to A_C. The location of the minimum value of M'_1 must be further from A_C than S_C is from A_C and it must be closer to S_C than it is to A_C. This often makes it possible to "guess" the approximate location of a measure of average position based on a positive areal moment where it is either undesirable or impossible to perform the actual computations. To make it even more useful the rule can be generalized. If λ_y is the measure of average position based on the yth positive areal moment and λ_z is the measure of average position based on the zth positive areal moment and $y > z$, then λ_y must be closer to A_C and closer to λ_z than λ_z is to A_C.

The Median Center

The *Median Center*, MD_C, of an areal population is the location of the minimum value of M'_1. This is the areal counterpart of the median in linear statistics which has a similar property. The median is that point on the axis of the variable in a linear frequency distribution such that the sum of the absolute deviations of the values of the items of the population from this point is a minimum. Since areal deviations are distances on the surface of a sphere, the median center is often called the point of minimum average travel or minimum aggregate travel.

The history of this measure is the story of a continual process of confusion and correction. The first attempts at using the concept of a median for areal analysis were based on the median's property of dividing a population in half. Thus, a "median point" was defined as the intersection of two orthogonal axes each of which divides the population in half. However, the location of this intersection depends on the direction of the axes. This feature was first recognized

---

[2]Further examples of this characteristic of S_C and A_C can be found in Mackay [63]. This article also contains valuable comments about the selection of control points.

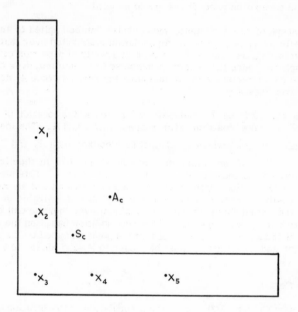

FIGURE 4.—Example Showing the Arithmetic Mean Center
Outside the Area Being Considered

by Hayford [47] in 1902. He wrote that there are an infinite number of median points corresponding to the infinite possible directions and that the points were not all confined in so small an area that the differences could be ignored. This is illustrated in *Figure 5* where three pairs of orthogonal axes dividing the population of 17 items in half were drawn. The result is three distinct median points.

Another disadvantage of this measure is that large movements of the population within one quadrant will not affect the location of the median point but any movement from one quadrant to another will change its location. Because of these two features the median point is virtually useless as a measure of average position. Since this has been stated many times in the last fifty years, it is dismaying to read a recent paper by Hart ([46], p. 56) in which he says that "the median point . . . is probably the best single index of centrality for a single areal distribution".

Interest in MD_C as the point of minimum aggregate travel distance arose as the consequence of an error made by the United States Bureau of the Census. In the 1920's the Bureau used the following definition of the arithmetic mean center in addition to the center of gravity definition: "If all the people in the United States were to be assembled at one place, the center of population would be the point which they could reach with the minimum aggregate travel, assuming that they all traveled in direct lines from their residences to the meeting place".[3] Gini and Galvani [39] supplied the proper definitions of S_C and MD_C in 1929. Gini repeated this argument in English a year later when he stated: "In the same article it is also noted that the designation of 'median point' should properly be given to the point of minimum aggregate travel, and not to the intersection of two orthogonal median lines, which intersection is not invariant with respect to the system of coordinates to which the points of the plane are referred". Eells [31] also pointed out the error in the Bureau of the Census' definition at about the same time.

These comments should have ended the controversy concerning the definitions of S_C and MD_C. Unfortunately, errors continued to appear and in 1948 Haldane ([44], p. 414) emphasized that the median center "is the point the sum of whose distances from the representative points of the sample is a minimum". By 1961, incorrect and misleading definitions of the Bureau's "center of population" still were appearing in print.[4] Happily, this situation recently has been rectified and the Census Bureau's [105] definition has been modified so that it should no

---

[3]Sloane [84], p. 7.

[4]See the *New York Times*, April 12, 1961, pp. 1, 27. This is a report of a press conference held by Secretary of Commerce Luther H. Hodges. Two definitions of the Bureau of the Census' center of population are listed in this article as having been mentioned by Secretary Hodges. Unfortunately, neither defines the arithmetic mean center that was computed at the Bureau. One is a definition of MD_C while the other describes a "median point".

The official definition that has been used by the Bureau of the Census can be found in many government publications. For example, see the U. S. Bureau of the Census [106], p. 9. While this definition is nearly correct the last phrase is subject to misinterpretation. This states that each individual exerts "an influence on the central point proportional to his distance from the point". This is true only if distances are measured with respect to a rectangular coordinate system. If distances between two positions are measured directly (the way they are in this study) the influence is proportional to the *square* of his distance from the point.

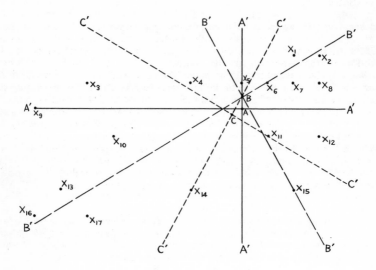

FIGURE 5.—"Median Points" of a Hypothetical Areal Distribution (A, B, and C are "median points" when the orthogonal axes are A', B', and C' respectively)

longer be misinterpreted. The center now is defined as "that point upon which the United States would balance, if it were a rigid plane, without weight and the population were distributed thereon with each individual being assumed to have equal weight".

The median center has the same four basic characteristics as the arithmetic mean center. The only important difference in properties between these two measures is that MD_c is less affected by extreme locations than S_c.

The usefulness of MD_c is based on the fact that it is the position of minimum average travel. Therefore, it is a theoretically optimum location for areal service centers in a region, such as schools, warehouses, garages, and meeting places. Of course, this is just a first approximation and the actual location of these facilities will be influenced by local conditions such as the actual network of roads, land values, traffic patterns, etc. The value of MD_c is that it can serve as a useful starting point from which the effects of these other factors can be analyzed.

The Modal Center

Although most measures of average position are based on areal moments, parameters that bear no necessary relationship to moments can be devised. Perhaps the most important of these is the *modal center, MO_c*

For a linear frequency distribution the mode is the value on the axis of the variable directly beneath the high point on the frequency curve; it can be simply defined as the most common value of the variable for the given population. An inspection of the graph of the frequency curve usually will reveal the approximate location of the mode. However, in practice it cannot be assumed that the mode is exactly at the mid-value of the class with the greatest frequency because this would be entirely dependent upon the choice of the class interval. This difficulty is overcome by the process of curve fitting to smooth the irregularities of the distribution. The precise value of the mode can be determined only by using the mathematical equation which describes the continuous curve of "closest possible fit" for the given frequency distribution. The mode is the value on the axis of the variable directly beneath the maximum on this ideal curve.

A similar situation exists when one attempts to find a modal center for an areally distributed population. Density of population, the areal counterpart of frequency, is in the limit arbitrary for a population composed of discrete items. If classes were selected that were just large enough to accomodate one item each, every class would fall into one of two density categories—one item per class area or no items per class area. A map portraying such a density pattern would be virtually the same as a dot map. Consequently, a smoothed surface for an areal density distribution must be developed so that the areal density of population can be expressed by some mathematical function at any point in the area. Of course, density at a point is inconceivable—it really means the number of items of the population in an appropriately sized unit area in which the point lies. The modal center can then be defined as the high point on such a surface, meaning that areal density is at a maximum in the unit area centered on this point.

Using a smoothed surface, it is possible to draw a map showing iso-lines of equal density. However, it must be remembered that this continuous variable only represents a mathematical model and actual density is still discrete. Moreover, density is still a microgeographic variable since a truly macrogeographic variable must be areally continuous, and its value at any point must depend on the location of every item in the population.

In linear statistics, most actual curves of closest possible fit are unimodal and the value of the mode can be calculated without much difficulty. For areal distributions, such is not the case. Even the "smoothed" surfaces often have several peaks. In some instances one of these peaks is significantly higher than the others and its location can be regarded as the modal center. Unfortunately, there are many cases where this cannot be done and it must be concluded that there is no single meaningful MO_c for such a distribution.

When a satisfactory modal center can be found, this parameter has several characteristics that are much different from those possessed by either S_c or MD_c:

1. MO_c obviously must be within the area under consideration.

2. MO_c does reveal information about the region where it is located. By definition of the modal center, this region must have the highest density in the whole area. It also can be assumed to have the features that are usually associated with high density for the variable under consideration.

3. MO_c is the least sensitive of all measures of average position. Almost none of the movements within a population will affect its location.

The chief value of the modal center comes from the second of these characteristics. It can be used most advantageously for comparing the location of density peaks of several variables for a given region. Unlike S_c, the modal center can be used as a basis for planning decisions since the location of the peak density is a major factor in the analysis of any areal variable.

Its insensitivity makes the modal center almost completely useless for analysis of changing areal patterns over time. In addition, MO_c is a microscopic parameter, based on the location of only a part of the population. This impairs its usefulness even more.

The Harmonic Mean Center

The *harmonic mean center*, H_c, is the position of the minimum value of $\sqrt[-1]{M'_{-1}}$. This also can be expressed as the location of the minimum value of $\dfrac{1}{\dfrac{\displaystyle\sum_{x=1}^{P}\left(\dfrac{1}{r_{jx}}\right)}{P}}$. Although this form is more complex it makes it easier to see that H_c is analogous to the harmonic mean for linear distributions which is the reciprocal of the arithmetic mean of the reciprocals of the values of the items in the population.

Inverse moments are rarely used in linear statistics because of one severe limitation: they are not truly continuous variables since meaningful values of inverse moments cannot be calculated about positions on the axis where items of the population are located. This is true because the "distance" from a unit of the population to its own position on the axis of the variable is zero, and the reciprocal of zero is infinity. Thus, the arithmetic mean of the reciprocals (the inverse first moment) would have a value of infinity at such points. Happily, this condition does not hold for areal distributions. Each item of an areal population occupies some finite, measurable portion of area. Hence, there are no zero deviations entering into the calculations of areal moments (as well as no negative deviations, by definition).

This is only one reason why the harmonic mean center plays a far more important role than its often-ignored linear counterpart. For an areal frequency distribution H_c is located at the minimum value of

$$\frac{\sum_{i=1}^{N} \left(\frac{p_i}{r_{ij}}\right)}{P} = \frac{P}{\sum_{i=1}^{N} \left(\frac{p_i}{r_{ij}}\right)}. \text{ Since}$$

P is a constant for a given population, H_c can be defined as located at the mini-

mum value of $\dfrac{1}{\sum_{i=1}^{N} \left(\dfrac{p_i}{r_{ij}}\right)}$. If λ is an areally distributed variable whose values

must be greater than zero, the minimum value of λ must be located at the same point as the maximum value of $\frac{1}{\lambda}$. Therefore, H_c also can be written as the loca-

tion of the maximum value of $\sum_{i=1}^{N} \left(\dfrac{p_i}{r_{ij}}\right)$ when grouped data are used.[5] This expres-

sion is the formula for the location of the peak of potential of population.[6]

Potential of population is the basic variable of the gravity model used in social physics. When human properties are considered, the peak of potential of population has been found to be the hub of socio-economic activity for an area.[7] Hence, H_c becomes a very important measure in the study of human areal populations. This relationship also adds to the usefulness of the peak of potential, since the fact that this peak has certain statistical properties akin to the harmonic mean can now be utilized.

H_c has two other important characteristics—it must be located within the area under consideration and it is insensitive to movements within the population. These properties are very similar to those listed for the modal center. In fact, for most areal distributions H_c and MO_c will coincide. Although this does not have to be true, there are only two types of distributions where these two centers

---

[5] For ungrouped data H_c would be located at the maximum value of $\sum_{x=1}^{P} \left(\dfrac{1}{r_{jx}}\right)$.

[6] Warntz and Neft [119], p. 50.

[7] This has been demonstrated in several studies. See especially Stewart [86, 87, 89] and Stewart and Warntz [95, 96].

do not coincide. These are multi-modal distributions where MO_c is surrounded by a large area of relatively low density or where MO_c is at an extreme location with respect to the rest of the population. These situations rarely occur in actual distributions.

In comparing H_c and MO_c, the harmonic mean center has all the advantages. H_c is based on an areal moment which is a macrogeographic variable, areally continuous, and including the locations of every item in the population in its calculation. However, it must be remembered that H_c is still insensitive because many of these locations can be changed without moving H_c. Unlike MO_c, H_c is always calculable and unique. Thus the deficiencies of MO_c as a measure of average position become much less important since the harmonic mean center can always be used in preference to the modal center.

Since it is insensitive to internal movement, H_c cannot be used to indicate the gradual changing of an areal pattern over time. As H_c indicates the "hub" or center of activity of a distribution, its movements are likely to be sudden large shifts from one region of very high density to another. Therefore, the principal value of H_c in time series analysis is to indicate when there have been shifts in the location of the hub and to serve as a basis for predicting when another such shift may occur.

H_c can also be used like MO_c for the comparison of several variables for a given area and as a basis for planning decisions when the location of the hub is a major factor. In addition, H_c has a wide range of uses when it is considered as part of the whole distribution of potential of population. These will be discussed in some detail in Chapter V.

Other Measures of Average Position

The arithmetic mean center, median center, modal center, and harmonic mean center are the most important measures of average position. There are also several centers that are used only occasionally but which still merit some attention.

The *geometric mean center*, G_c, is defined as the location of the minimum value of the antilog of the arithmetic mean of the logarithms of distances to the items of the population. This is analagous to the concept of the geometric mean in linear statistics. In practice this definition can be simplified since both the division by P and the use of antilogs are superfluous for defining this center. Thus, G_c is located at the minimum value of $\sum_{x=1}^{P} (log\ r_{jx})$. For grouped data this expression becomes $\sum_{i=1}^{N} (p_i\ log\ r_{ij})$.

G_c possesses some of the same properties as S_c and MD_c. It does not have to be in the area under consideration, it does not necessarily indicate any characteristics of the region where it is located, and any movement within the population will cause some change in its location. However, one additional factor severely limits the usefulness of G_c. Since the logarithms of distances are employed, large differences in distances have very little effect on G_c. For example, if $r_1 = 1000$ miles and $r_2 = 3000$ miles, $log\ r_1 \div log\ r_2 = 0.863$. While a measure of average position should not be *excessively* influenced by extreme locations, the opposite also is undesirable. Hence, G_c should be used only when there is a specific reason for letting distance play a minor role.

When G_c is used, a guide to its approximate location can be borrowed from a rule of linear statistics. When all observations have positive values that are not all the same the geometric mean must lie between the arithmetic mean and the harmonic mean. This can be applied to the areal case where it means that G_c must be closer to both c and H_c than S_c is to H_c.

Returning to the concept of measures of average position based on areal moments, a *third moment center*, III_c, can be defined as the location of the minimum value of $\sqrt[3]{M_3'}$, or more simply, the location of the minimum value of M_3'. This is rarely used because it is in no way superior to S_c, and it has the disadvantage of being even more influenced by extreme locations than S_c.

Similarly, an infinite number of centers based on positive areal moments could be listed. For example, the *fourth moment center*, IV_c, is the location of the minimum value of M_4'. However, as the number of the moment increases, the effect of extreme locations increases very rapidly. As a result, III_c and IV_c are rarely used, and measures of average position based on higher positive moments have never been used.

Some social scientists have tried using a so-called gravity model based on the inverse second areal moment. The *inverse second moment center*, $-II_c$, is located at the minimum value of $\sqrt[-2]{M_{-2}'}$. This can be described as the location of the maximum value of $\sum_{x=1}^{P} \left(\frac{1}{r_{jx}^2} \right)$ or, for grouped data, $\sum_{i=1}^{N} \left(\frac{p_i}{r_{ij}^2} \right)$. In almost all cases this will coincide with H_c. Since no one has ever demonstrated that this center has any advantages over H_c and the *true* gravity model, the inverse second moment center is seldom used.

The only other measure of average position that has been used was introduced by Scates [81] in 1933. He called attention to a center which would indicate the minimum variability of travel distances. This *variance center*, VR_c, is located at the minimum value of $\dfrac{\sum_{x=1}^{P} \left(\left[r_{jx} - (M_1' \text{ at } j) \right]^2 \right)}{P}$. For grouped data this becomes the location of the minimum value of $\dfrac{\sum_{i=1}^{N} \left[p_i \left(\left[r_{ij} - (M_1' \text{ at } j) \right]^2 \right) \right]}{P}$. VR_c tends to be located in a region of very low density since many low values of r_{jx} result in a large value for the variance of r. VR_c will be located at a position approximately equidistant from the regions of high density in the area. However, the actual distance from VR_c to these high density regions can be very great. Therefore, for most areal distributions, VR_c is outside of the area that is being considered. This makes VR_c a virtually useless measure.

A brief example will serve to illustrate this principle. For the 1960 human population of the United States, VR_c was located in the northwestern part of the Canadian province of Manitoba. The variance of r at that point was less than 90,000 miles squared. The lowest value of the variance of r within the United States was approximately 100,000 miles squared, at the border between Manitoba and eastern North Dakota. However, the value at the North Pole also was approximately 100,000 miles squared! It seems safe to conclude that the location of VR_c does not necessarily reveal any information about the areal distribution of a population.

Some Applications of Measures of Average Position

As stated in Chapter I, measures that are mentioned in this work will be applied to the areal distributions of the human populations of seven nations in order to make some comparisons among these distributions. *Table 2* shows some of the preliminary data for these distributions. The countries are listed in inverse order of the size of their populations at the given date. D_A is the average density over the area and it is equal to P divided by A. Another useful parameter is r_A which indicates the size of the area in units of distance. If the area is assumed to be a circle with area A, r_A is the length of the radius of that circle. Thus,

$$r_A = \sqrt{\frac{A}{\pi}} \, .$$

Demographers often have found it useful to eliminate portions of an area that are virtually uninhabited from the analysis of the distribution of population. The United States Bureau of the Census defines the "effectively settled area", a, as that portion of the total area with a density of at least two persons per square mile. This is the definition that will be used in this study. Then D_a can be

defined as $\frac{P}{a}$ and $r_a = \sqrt{\frac{a}{\pi}}$. The value of this concept will be demonstrated in

Chapter VIII when certain measures of dispersion and skewness will be compared to r_A and r_a.

All the measures of average position that have been discussed are shown in *Figure 6* for the United States population in 1960. Six of these, S_C, A_C, a_C (the center of gravity of the effectively settled area), MD_C, MO_C, and H_C are shown for the other six nations in *Figures 7* through *12*. Most of the features of these centers can be seen by inspecting the maps. However, some of the more interesting characteristics will be listed here for additional emphasis:

1. The populations tend to be concentrated near the oceans. The modal centers, New York City, Sydney, London, Rio de Janeiro, Tokyo, Calcutta, and Shanghai are all ports.

2. For six of the seven distributions MO_C and H_C coincide. India is an example of a multi-modal distribution where the modal center, Calcutta, has only a slightly greater density than Bombay. H_C is located at Kanpur in the heart of the high density Ganges river valley.

3. In none of these cases are all six centers very close together. India becomes the lone exception if MO_C is disregarded as having little significance in this case.

4. S_C and MD_C usually are fairly close to each other.

TABLE 2

POPULATION AND AREA DATA FOR SEVEN NATIONS

Nation	Date	P (millions of persons)	A (thousands of square miles)	D_A (persons per square mile)	r_A (miles)	a (thousands of square miles)	D_a (persons per square mile)	r_a (miles)
Australia	1947	7.58	2975	2.5	973	447	17	377
United Kingdon	1951	50.2	93.98	535	173	93.98	535	173
Brazil	1950	51.9	3288	16	1023	1347	39	655
Japan	1955	89.3	142.8	625	213	142.8	625	213
United States	1960	178.5	2975	60	973	2508	71	893
India	1957	390	1257	311	633	1143	342	603
China	1957	639	3897	164	1114	1890	338	776

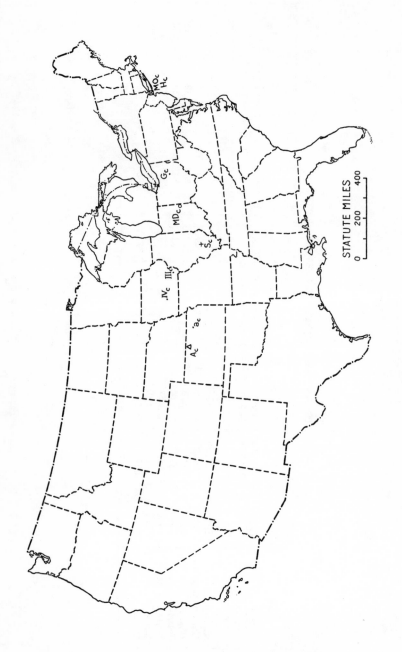

FIGURE 6. — Average Positions for the Distribution of Population in the United States, 1960

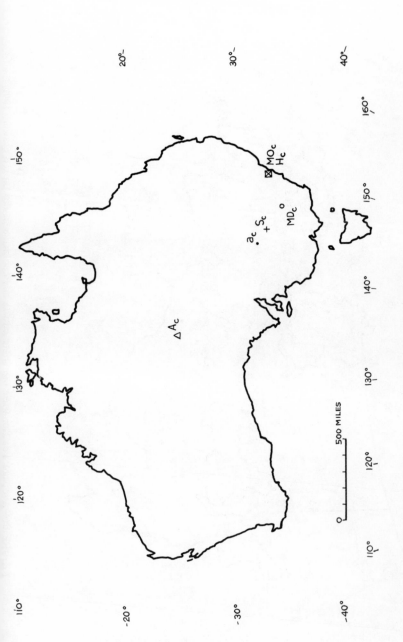

FIGURE 7.—Average Positions for the Distribution of Population in Australia, 1947

42

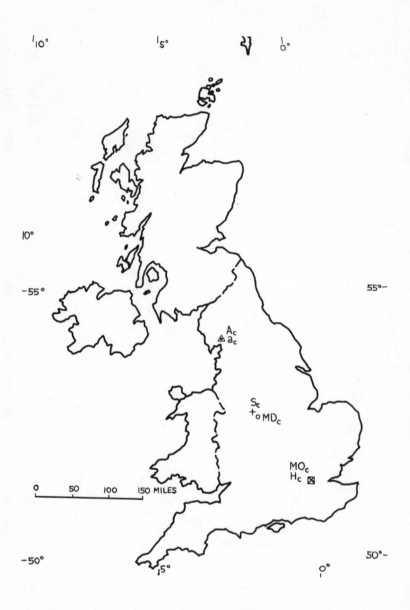

FIGURE 8.—Average Positions for the Distribution of Population
in the United Kingdom, 1951

FIGURE 9.—Average Positions for the Distribution of Population
in Brazil, 1950

44

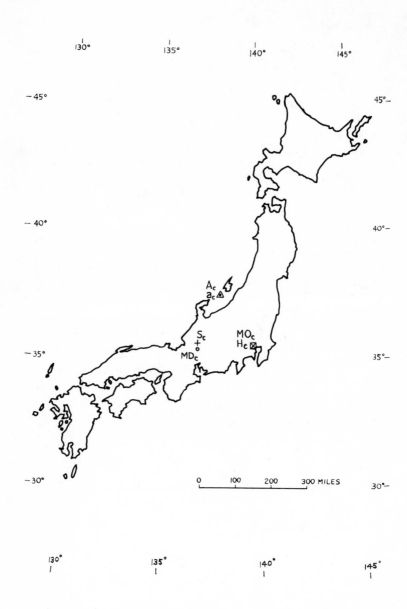

Figure 10.—Average Positions for the Distribution of Population
in Japan, 1955

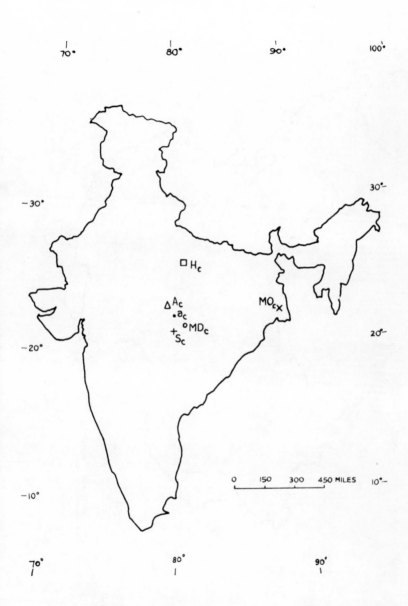

FIGURE 11.—Average Positions for the Distribution of Population
in India, 1957

46

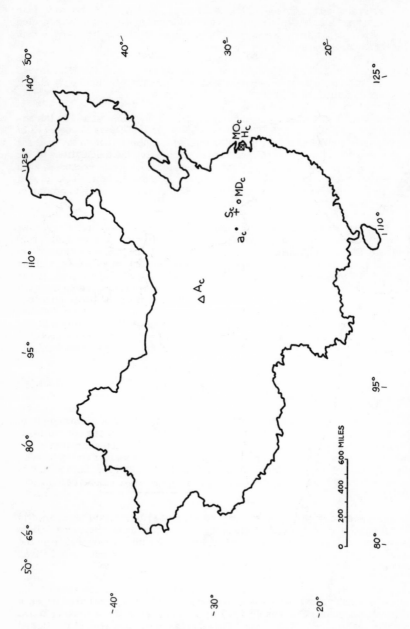

FIGURE 12. — Average Positions for the Distribution of Population in China, 1957

5. In every case where a is less than A, a_c is closer to S_c and MD_c than A_c is to S_c and MD_c. This is perfectly logical since it is to be expected that most of the sparsely inhabited areas would not be near the high density regions.

6. Japan provides an illustration of the fact that several of these measures do not have to be located within the area. For this distribution A_c and a_c are in the Sea of Japan.

Interpretation of these maps also must depend, to some extent, on the accuracy of the locations of these centers. There are three possible sources of error. The most important of these is the probable amount of error in the original data—the censuses and population estimates upon which the calculations of the centers were based. Even in the case of recent United States censuses, such errors may be sizable in some areas. When China and India are considered, inaccuracies are almost surely quite large. Unfortunately, there is no way of measuring the magnitude of these errors.

Secondly, inaccuracies can occur in the computation of measures of average position from given data. Quantitative estimates of such errors can be made from a knowledge of the computational procedure employed, the number of classes in the various areal frequency distributions, the selection of control points, and the accuracy of the measurements of distance. H_c and MO_c are always located in the heart of major cities when human populations are being considered so they are very accurately located. The calculations of S_c, A_c, and a_c are based on a tremendous number of classes and very accurate procedures so that computational errors in these cases are small—probably not more than ten miles in any instance. For MD_c this error can be important. It may range from a probable maximum of ten miles for the United Kingdom to as much as fifty miles for India and China.

The final source of error occurs in the plotting of the calculated positions on the maps. However, these are of relatively minor consequence.

While these errors may be relatively small, they do exist and attempts to overstate the accuracy of the determination of these centers are not justified. For example, federal tax funds were used to finance the determination of the exact location of the 1960 arithmetic mean center of the United States population by a triangulation party from the Coast and Geodetic Survey. Such action is obviously ridiculous, as it implies both a perfectly accurate census and perfect calculation of S_c.

Measures of average position can be also used to indicate the change in areal patterns over a period of time. In this section these measures will be applied to the human population of the United States for twenty periods, from the colonial year of 1754 until 1960. The basic data for these distributions are given in *Table 3*.

Figure 13 is a graph showing r_A and r_a for each of these years. This emphatically demonstrates the distribution between A and a. Total area depends on political decisions. Changes in total area occur suddenly because of wars, revolutions, political dealings, etc. The increases in the area of the United States were due to the wars between England and France in the 1760's, the

TABLE 3

POPULATION AND AREA DATA FOR THE UNITED STATES, 1754–1960

Date	P (millions of persons)	A (thousands of square miles)	D_A (persons per square mile)	r_A (miles)	a (thousands of square miles)	D_a (persons per square mile)	r_a (miles)
1754	1.43	236	6.0	274	130	11	204
1775	2.46	865	2.8	526	184	13	242
1790	3.93	865	4.5	526	239	16	276
1800	5.31	865	6.1	526	306	17	312
1810	7.24	1682	4.3	733	408	18	360
1820	9.64	1750	5.5	747	509	19	402
1830	12.9	1750	7.4	747	633	20	449
1840	17.1	1750	9.8	747	807	21	507
1850	23.2	2940	7.9	968	979	24	558
1860	31.4	2970	11	973	1195	26	617
1870	38.6	2970	13	973	1272	30	636
1880	50.2	2970	17	973	1570	32	707
1890	62.9	2970	21	973	1947	32	787
1900	76.0	2970	26	973	1926	39	783
1910	92.0	2970	31	973	2249	41	846
1920	105.7	2969	36	973	2356	45	866
1930	122.8	2977	41	973	2410	51	876
1940	131.7	2977	44	973	2474	53	887
1950	150.7	2975	51	973	2508	60	893
1960	178.5	2975	60	973	2508	71	893

49

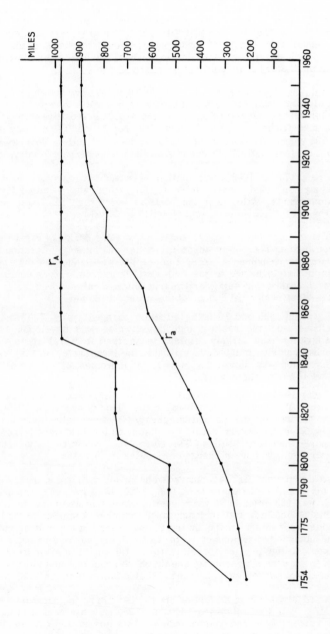

FIGURE 13. — r_A and r_a — United States, 1754-1960

Louisiana Purchase in 1803, the acquisition of Florida between 1810 and 1820, and the annexation of Texas, the Mexican Cession and the Gadsden Purchase in the 1840's and the 1850's. Effectively settled area, however, depends on physical, social and economic conditions and tends to change gradually. The graph of r_a indicates the gradual development of the area of the United States rather than the history of its political boundaries.

The changing locations of S_c, A_c, MD_c, MO_c and H_c are shown in *Figure 14.* Unfortunately, a_c could not be shown because comparable density maps are not available for all the necessary dates. S_c and MD_c, the sensitive measures, can be used to indicate the gradual movement of the population. The net movement of S_c in the 206 years between 1754 and 1960 has been 732 miles. This can be subdivided to form four distinct periods of American demographic history.

1. From 1754 to 1790 the population increased but remained concentrated along the east coast. Internal migration was a minor factor and immigrants settled near the ports at which they entered the country. The net movement of S_c was 48 miles in 36 years.

2. The century between 1790 and 1890 was the period of great westward expansion. There was an open frontier and internal migration became a mass phenomenon. Many immigrants who landed on the east coast immediately moved to the mid-west. Immigrants began coming to the west coast from Asia, particularly China. S_c also moved faster toward the West, with a net change of 507 miles in 100 years.

3. Between 1890 and 1940 the situation changed again. The frontier had closed and the eastern industrial region was developing. Internal migration was largely confined to shifts from rural areas to nearby urban centers. Immigrants settled in the large eastern cities. Westward expansion was slower and so was the movement of S_c. The net change was 102 miles in 50 years.

4. From 1940 to 1960, regional economic differences were the dominant force. The Pacific Coast became the "land of opportunity". While the percentage of the population engaged in interstate migration in this period was not very great, the distances involved were large, usually more than 1500 miles. Therefore, the westward movement of S_c increased, with a net change of 81 miles in 20 years.

So that this pattern may be compared with that for a different area, *Figure 15* shows S_c for Brazil in the years 1872, 1890, 1920, 1940 and 1950. The net movement of S_c was 182 miles in 78 years over an area similar in size to the United States. This period in Brazilian demographic history is similar to the last half of the eighteenth century in the United States. There has been little movement toward the uninhabited regions of western Brazil and the frontier has not really been opened. If the physical barriers to settlement in interior Brazil can be overcome, that nation may someday see the phenomenon of mass internal migration similar to that which took place in the United States between 1790 and 1890.

Westward expansion in the United States also can be indicated by the movement of MD_c until 1890. Between 1890 and 1960 MD_c has remained in a small region in western Ohio and eastern Indiana. This further supports the previous observation that the closing of the frontier occurred around 1890.

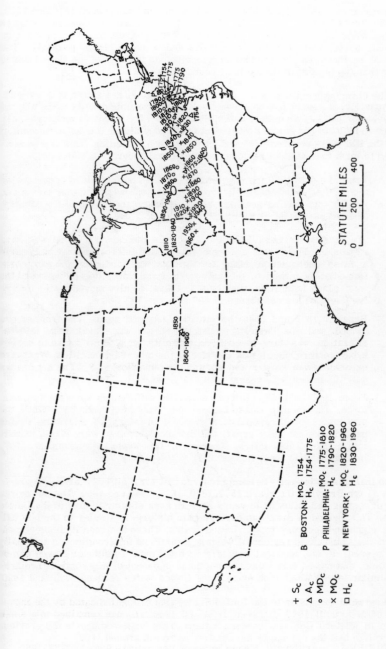

FIGURE 14.—Average Positions for the Distribution of Population in the United States, 1754–1960

FIGURE 15.—Arithmetic Mean Center of Population—Brazil, 1872-1950

The period between 1940 and 1960 seems to present a contradiction—S_C moved rapidly westward while MD_C remained practically stationary. This can be explained by examining the pattern of internal migration. Since S_C is based on M_2' and MD_C is based on M_1', large distances are much more heavily weighted in the calculation of S_C. Thus, the movement in S_C is the result of the rapid increase in population near the Pacific Coast. Where MD_C is concerned, this factor is balanced by the very low absolute increase in population in the area between the Rocky Mountains and the Mississippi River and the relatively large absolute increase in population in the industrial northeast and middle west. It is important to remember that these centers are affected only by absolute changes in the population. Percentage increases are meaningless in this case.

The insensitive centers, MO_C and H_C, can be used to examine the shifts in the location of the chief city or "hub" of the United States. Since 1754 only three cities have been the modal center and the harmonic mean center of the United States population. In 1754, both H_C and MO_C were located in Boston. By 1775 MO_C had shifted to Philadelphia while H_C was still in Boston. From 1790 through 1810 both these centers were in Philadelphia. By 1820 the last shift had begun and MO_C was in New York. Since 1830 both H_C and MO_C have been located in New York City.

It is interesting to note that in both cases MO_C moved before H_C. This lead-lag relationship is not necessary, but it usually occurs. The customary pattern is for density to increase rapidly in a small area, causing a shift in MO_C. Then density begins to increase in the surrounding regions which may cause H_C to move to the same location as MO_C. For example, if current rates of population increase in the major United States cities continue for the next few decades, Los Angeles may become the modal center. However, this trend will not be nearly great enough to cause H_C to shift to the west coast. Such a shift would require a tremendous change in the pattern of population distribution in the United States. If every person in the United States who lived within 1000 miles of Los Angeles in 1960 were treated as *three* people, the values of the inverse first moment at New York City and Los Angeles would have been approximately equal. Thus, the whole western population would have to increase by more than 200% (almost 60 million people) without any increase in population in the eastern two-thirds of the country to cause H_C to shift to Los Angeles.[8]

Such an occurrence is extremely unlikely in the forseeable future. H_C will surely remain at New York City for at least the remainder of this century. The belief has been expressed[9] that large scale internal migration to the west coast will cease around the year 2000. If this should prove to be true, New York City may be the harmonic mean center of the distribution of the human population in this area for the next few centuries.

---

[8]These figures are based on the assumption that the pattern of distribution within these two broad areas remains the same.

[9]Warntz [114], Chapter 5.

CHAPTER V
MEASURES OF DISPERSION

In the preceding chapter several measures of average position were defined as the location of the minimum or maximum values of certain areally distributed variables. Thus, one point represented an entire areal distribution. Of course, this was directly analagous to the linear statistical method by which a single measure of central tendency can represent all the items in a linear distribution. However, for many purposes of analysis these averages, while valuable, are not sufficient. Additional measures are needed to supplement the average and to indicate the manner in which the individual items are dispersed about the particular average.

Measures of dispersion in linear statistics are based on some method of averaging the differences or deviations between the values of the individual items and some average value for the whole distribution. For areal distributions measures of dispersion about average positions are simply certain averages of the distances from the individual units of the population to the appropriate average position.

The Standard Distance Deviation

One of the basic measures of dispersion in linear statistics is the *root-mean-square deviation* of the values of the items of the population about any one value. As its name suggests this is found by taking the square root of the arithmetic mean of the squares of the differences between the individual values and the assumed value. Obviously this is the square root of the second statistical moment about a point. Since the minimum value of the second statistical moment occurs at the arithmetic mean, the root-mean-square deviation also must be at a minimum about the arithmetic mean. This special case of the root-mean-square deviation is called the *standard deviation*.

Similar definitions can be employed for areal distributions. The *root-mean-square distance deviation* is simply $\sqrt{M_2'}$. When computed about the arithmetic mean center, $\sqrt{M_2'}$, is a minimum and can be called the *standard distance deviation, S_r*.

The values of areal moments computed about S_c have certain valuable properties that are related to model surfaces.[1] To facilitate future explanations, M_n', when computed about S_c, will henceforth be designated as M_n. Thus, S_r can be defined simply as $\sqrt{M_2}$.

In linear statistics, the square of the standard deviation is the *variance* of the distribution. Similarly, M_2, the square of S_r, can be called the *distance variance* of an areal distribution.

---

[1]See pp.

The pattern of the notation system used in this work now becomes more apparent. Every measure of average position has the subscript "c" for "center" All measures of dispersion have the subscript "r", denoting that they are in units of distance. In addition, measures of average position and measures of dispersion based on the same concept or the same areal moment have the same basic symbol. For example, both the arithmetic mean center and the standard distance deviation are based on the second areal moment. Hence the symbols S_c and S_r.

A bivariate measure analogous to S_r was first proposed by Furfey [36] in 1927 for use in ecology. However, Furfey did not apply his measure and it attracted little attention for a generation. Recently, Bachi ([5], pp. 5-12) has revived this measure and called it the *standard distance*. The standard distance is related to the usual bivariate standard deviation. They differ by a constant[2] equal to $\sqrt{2}$.

Stewart and Warntz ([95], p. 182) introduced S_r as the *dynamical radius* in 1958. This is simply the univariate version of Bachi's standard distance.[3] This name was used because, in physics, the value of the second moment is related to the preponderance of kinetic versus potential energy. Thus, the second physical moment is used to measure the expansion or contraction of a body. Similarly, for areal distributions S_r is usually employed to indicate the expansion or contraction of the population as a whole over a period of time. In this way S_r serves to supplement S_c. Together they can be used to present a clear, meaningful, quantitative description of the changes in the areal pattern of a population over time.

This measure is also important when hypotheses based on sample statistics are being tested. In particular, the standard distance deviation of a sampling distribution of arithmetic mean centers (called the *standard error of the arithmetic mean center*) will be used in such tests in Chapter IX.

S_r^2 is, of course, the value of the second areal moment at only one point (S_c). In addition to the characteristics of this measure, the entire distribution of M_2' has several interesting properties. When small areas are being considered, the sphericity of the earth can be safely ignored and M_2' can be shown to be functionally related to M_2. This relationship is based on the Pythagorean Theorem and requires only that M_2 and the distance between S_c and j, r_{cj}, be known in order to calculate M_2' at j. The formula is: M_2' at $j = M_2 + r_{cj}^2$. This produces a map of the second areal moment where the isolines are concentric circles about S_c. All patterns of the distribution of the population, regardless of lack of symmetry, produce this symmetrical map of M_2'. M_2' is the only areal moment that has this characteristic.

---

[2] Bivariate standard deviation $(\sigma) = \sqrt{\dfrac{\sigma_x^2 + \sigma_y^2}{2}}$ where σ_x^2 and σ_y^2 are the variances of variables x and y respectively. The standard distance $= \sqrt{\sigma_x^2 + \sigma_y^2}$. Therefore, the standard distance $= \sqrt{2}\sigma$.

[3] If the sphericity of the earth is ignored $S_r = \sqrt{\sigma_x^2 + \sigma_y^2}$ because of the Pythagorean Theorem and S_r = the standard distance.

For large areas, these results are affected by the fact that the earth is a sphere. However, even for an area as large as China or the United States the above formula provides an extremely accurate estimate of M_2'. In the case of the human population of the United States, the error in M_2' at any point that would result from ignoring the sphericity of the earth would be less than one-half of one percent of the value of M_2'. This is well within the probable amount of error caused by grouping the data into an areal frequency distribution. In addition, the direction of this error is known since distance calculated by the Pythagorean Theorem can never be less than the shortest great circle distance between the same two points as measured on the surface of a sphere. Therefore, $(M_2'$ at $j) \leq M_2' + r_{cj}^2$.

A map depicting the isolines of the second areal moment as concentric circles is similarly an extremely close approximation to reality in almost all instances. Unfortunately, such a map, while easy to compute and draw, has little usefulness. Just as the location of S_c is not related to the characteristics of the region near S_c, the isolines of M_2' are not related to the areal pattern of the distribution of the population. For example, in the case of the 1960 human population of the United States, the isoline of M_2' that passes through New York City also passes through parts of Wells county, North Dakota; the suburbs of Denver; Union county, New Mexico; the Gulf of Mexico; Lake county, Florida; the Atlantic Ocean; and three provinces of Canada. Clearly, these regions do not possess similar demographic, economic, or sociological characteristics. This disadvantage is a feature of the distributions of all positive areal moments.

The root-mean-square distance deviation about any point is an indication of the dispersion of the population about that point. However, the label "measure of dispersion" has usually been reserved for values about an appropriate center, such as S_γ which is the root-mean-square distance deviation about S_c. Of course, measures which depend on a particular reference point are not always the most useful parameters. This limitation can be overcome by defining general measures of dispersion that are based on the population's intrinsic spread. These measures will have the subscript "P" indicating that they refer to the whole population.

Each measure of dispersion can have a corresponding general measure of dispersion. The *general standard distance deviation*, S_P, is, like S_γ, based on M_2'. It can be expressed as $S_P = \left(\dfrac{\sum\limits_{i=1}^{N} \left[p_i \, (M_2' \text{ at } i) \right]}{P} \right)^{1/2}$ where i is the control point of class i. For ungrouped data this becomes $S_P = \left[\dfrac{\sum\limits_{x=1}^{P} (M_2' \text{ at } x)}{P} \right]^{1/2}$. There is one and only one value of S_P for a population. This value is only dependent on the spread of the items of the population among themselves and not on deviations from some average position. Like all measures of dispersion, S_P is in units of distance.

In practice, the above complex formulas for the calculation of S_P are rarely used. Yule and Kendall ([123], p. 147) have proven that the root-mean-square deviation averaged over a frequency distribution is equal to its standard deviation multiplied by $\sqrt{2}$. The Pythagorean Theorem can be used to apply this proof to the areal case, so that $S_P = \sqrt{2} S_\gamma$. Thus, the distance variance, S_γ^2, may be defined as half the *general distance variance,* S_P^2 where S_P^2 is the mean square of the distance between all the possible pairs of items in the population. Of course, this relationship also ignores the effect of the sphericity of the earth. Once again, however, this effect will be minute for virtually all distributions. An exact statement of the above expression would be $S_P \leq \sqrt{2} S_\gamma$. Grouping errors are usually large enough so that accuracy cannot be improved by using the long formula to compute S_P. A sufficiently accurate approximation can be obtained by assuming $S_P = \sqrt{2} S_\gamma$.

Since S_P is so closely related to S_γ, they are rarely both used. S_P has the advantage of being independent of a particular reference point while S_γ has the advantage of being closely related to important and conventional measures in statistics.

The Mean Distance Deviation

The first areal moment also provides a valuable measure of dispersion. The value of M_1' at any point j is the arithmetic mean of the distances between all the items in the population and j. Thus, this has often been called the *mean convergence distance,* the *average distance,* or the *average travel distance* to j. The minimum value of M_1' or the *minimum average distance* occurs at MD_c. This value is the *mean distance deviation,* MD_γ. It is exactly analogous in concept to the *mean deviation* about the median in linear statistics.

The mean distance deviation serves to supplement the median center and both of these measures are most useful for one particular type of analysis. This is the problem of the selection of an optimum location in an area when one of the criteria for the selection is the minimization of distances to the location. In this type of problem MD_c is the position where the distances to all members of the population is a minimum and MD_γ is the arithmetic mean of the distances between the members of the population and MD_c. The addition of the measure of dispersion, MD_γ, aids the analysis in two ways. It provides an indication of the magnitude of the distances that are involved, and then this makes it possible to compare this magnitude with the values of MD_γ for other regions.

A map showing isolines of M_1' does not necessarily resemble a series of concentric circles. However, if an entire population was located at a point i, then $(M_n'$ at $j) = r_{ij}^n$. This means that if the population could be assumed to be located at one point, all areal moments would map as a series of concentric circles. For M_1' the validity of such an assumption increases as the distance from MD_c increases. Therefore, isolines on maps of M_1' tend to approach circularity when they are located at great distances from MD_c.

In Chapter III it was established that if the items of the population were scattered over an area, then $(M_n'$ at $j) > r_{cj}^n$ when $n > 0$. When $n = 1$ this becomes $(M_1'$ at $j) > r_{cj}$ which means that the mean convergence distance to any point must be greater than the distance between the median center and that point. However it is still true that the assumption that P is located at one point is more valid as the distance from MD_c increases. Thus, the difference between M_1' at j and r_{cj} decreases as r_{cj} increases.

This rule can be generalized to include all positive areal moments and it can be stated in a slightly different form. For $n>0$ the distance between equal differences in the values of M_n cannot increase as r_{cj} increases. This means that the distance between isolines on a map of a positive areal moment must either decrease or remain constant as r_{cj} increases, provided only that there is a constant interval of M_n' between isolines. This rule is a valuable aid in the construction of maps of positive areal moments.

The *general mean distance deviation*, MD_P, is the mean distance deviation averaged over the whole distribution and independent of the reference point, MD_C.

For ungrouped data $MD_P = \dfrac{\sum\limits_{x=1}^{P}\left[M_1' \ at \ x\right]}{P}$. When the data are in the form of an

areal frequency distribution, this expression becomes $MD_P = \dfrac{\sum\limits_{i=1}^{N}\left[P_i \ (M_1' \ at \ i)\right]}{P}$.

MD_P can also be described as the arithmetic mean distance between all possible pairs of items in the population. This is analagous to Gini's *mean difference* for linear distributions.

There is no functional relationship between MD_P and MD_r although the ratio of these measures has a limited range $(1 \leq \dfrac{MD_P}{MD_r} \leq 2)$. However, if P is large, MD_P is very close to $\sqrt{2}MD_r$. For the several dozen areal distributions of human populations of countries which have been studied by this researcher at the American Geographical Society, the ratio of MD_P to MD_r was between 1.35 and 1.47 in every case. The specific value within that range varies directly with K, the kurtosis of the populations. Thus, MD_P can be estimated from a knowledge of MD_r. Such an estimate often will prove to be at least as accurate as the value resulting from computing MD_P from grouped data.

This relationship also holds in linear statistics for the ratio of the mean difference to the mean deviation, when there are no negative values, although it seems to have been ignored. Kendall and Stuart ([57], pp. 7-51) have used an illustrative linear frequency distribution of the height of 8585 adult males in the British Isles. The mean distance of this distribution is 2.87619 inches and the mean deviation is 2.02353 inches. The ratio of the two measures is 1.421. However, this ratio and its closeness to $\sqrt{2}$ are not mentioned by Kendall and Stuart.

MD_P is a very useful measure because it represents the mean distance between all possible pairs of items in the population. It is particularly valuable for analyzing the degree of complexity of communication networks. For example, a population of an area could be considered to be composed of all cities with more than a specified number of people. Each city would be one member of the population. MD_P multiplied by $\dfrac{P(P-1)}{2}$ would be the total distance between all the possible pairs of cities. This value could then be compared to the total distance of highways or railroad tracks connecting these cities. The result could be compared to similar results for other areas, or at other times, or for other types of networks. This type of analysis might prove to be very useful for network planning.

The Harmonic Mean Distance Deviation

The last of the three most useful areal moments is the inverse first areal moment. As in the case of M_2' and M_1', there are also a series of three measures of dispersion based on M_{-1}'. The *reciprocal mean distance deviation* at any point is equal to $\sqrt[-1]{M_{-1}'}$ at that point. This value is a minimum at the harmonic mean center. Therefore, the *harmonic mean distance deviation*, H_γ, can be defined as the minimum value of $\sqrt[-1]{M_{-1}'}$. For human populations it is often convenient to define H_γ in terms of potential of population. In this case $H_\gamma = \dfrac{P}{V_c}$ where V_c is the peak potential of population at the harmonic mean center.[4] Similarly, the reciprocal mean distance deviation at a point j is equal to $\dfrac{P}{V_j}$.

H_γ is valuable because it indicates the dispersion about a very important position, H_c, the hub of the distribution. However, this measure has one major defect. When grouped data are used, the value of H_γ depends on the choice of classes and control points for the areal frequency distribution. In particular, H_γ is greatly influenced by the area of the class in which H_c is located. This factor limits the usefulness of H_γ although it can still be employed to provide an indication of the degree of concentration of the population around H_c.

The map of M_{-1}' is by far the most important of all the areal moment maps. This is the one case where the isolines of the moment distribution are related to the areal patterns of other phenomena. These relationships have been shown for human populations in many studies where M_{-1}' has been in the form of potential of population. Since $V_j = P(M_{-1}'$ at $j)$ the pattern of isolines of these two

---

[4] H_γ = minimum value of $\sqrt[-1]{M_{-1}'}$.

For grouped data, M_{-1}' at j = $\dfrac{\sum\limits_{i=1}^{N}\left(p_i\, r_{ij}^{-1}\right)}{P} = \dfrac{\sum\limits_{i=1}^{N}\left(\dfrac{p_i}{r_{ij}}\right)}{P}$.

$\sqrt[-1]{M_{-1}'}$ at j = $\dfrac{P}{\sum\limits_{i=1}^{N}\left(\dfrac{p_i}{r_{ij}}\right)}$.

But, V_j, the potential of population at j, = $\sum\limits_{i=1}^{N}\left(\dfrac{p_i}{r_{ij}}\right)$.

Therefore, $\sqrt[-1]{M_{-1}'}$ at j = $\dfrac{P}{V_j}$.

Let $j = H_c$.

$\sqrt[-1]{M_{-1}'}$ at $H_c = H_\gamma$.

$H_\gamma = \dfrac{P}{V_c}$ where V_c is the potential of population at H_c.

The form of this demonstration is the same for ungrouped data.

variables will be the same. Among the variables that have been found to be closely related to potential of population are the following:

1. Rural population density in the United Kingdom[5] in 1951.

2. Residences of college students in the United States.[6]

3. Many socio-economic variables for a large area within the United States in 1940, including:

   Rural population density
   Rural non-farm population density
   Rural non-farm rents
   Farmland values
   Density of railroad track
   Density of rural free delivery routes.[7]

4. Rural population density in the United States[8] in 1840, 1900, and 1930.

5. Rural population density in Mexico[9] in 1930.

6. County areas in the United States in 1790, 1860, 1900, and 1950, and area of parishes of the Episcopal Church in the United States[10] in 1850, 1900, and 1950.

Of course, the use of M'_{-1} is not restricted to human populations. Indeed, for the analysis of many socio-economic variables it is advisable to use personal income as the population. This has the effect of "weighting" each demographic unit by an economic factor. The distribution of this *income potential* in the United States in 1950 was found to be very closely related to the distributions of such variables as:

1. Income density

2. Telephone-wire density

3. Railroad-track density

4. Road density

5. Wholesale dry goods market area

6. Federal Reserve District area

7. State area

5Stewart and Warntz [96], pp. 110-113.

6Warntz [113, 117].

7Stewart and Warntz [95], p. 172.

8Stewart [90], pp. 482-485.

9Stewart [93], pp. 250-251.

10Stewart and Warntz [97].

8. County area

9. Size of farms

10. Value of farmland

11. Number of vehicles registered per mile of highway

12. Number of auto fatalities per registered vehicle

13. Ratio of individual taxes to income

14. Ratio of number of patents to income

15. Ratio of number of business failures to the total number of businesses.[11]

Calhoun [13] has used income potential in the United States in the 1940's in his study of social welfare. He found that income potential was associated with such factors as:

1. Percent of population employed in manufacturing

2. Percent of population living in the same house for one year

3. Percent of married couples without own household

4. Social Stressor Index

5. Aging-Mortality Index

6. Mortality from heart disease

7. Percent of population that is mentally ill

8. Physiological Stress Index.

The distribution of production and marketing of many commodities is related to potential and some illustrations of this will be presented in Chapter VIII. Studies at the American Geographical Society have revealed several other close associations between economic variables and the distribution of income potential in the United States. Some of the variables involved are retail sales, flow of bank checks, the ratio of time deposits to demand deposits in banks, per capita federal grants to state and local governments, and value added by manufacturing. In addition, potential of population and income potential have been used to analyze and predict patterns of migration,[12] political conflicts,[13] and patterns of world trade.[14]

---

[11]Stewart and Warntz [95], pp. 176-180.

[12]Warntz [114], Chapter 5.

[13]Stewart [91], Neft [70], Warntz [114], Chapter 7.

[14]Much of this material is included in unpublished papers by graduate students in geography at Hunter College, New York City.

The concept of the inverse first areal moment also has been extended to include additional variables. Harris [45] has used retail sales as a population for a *market potential*[15] in his analysis of the relationship between location of industry and location of market. A map of M'_1 based on transport costs also was employed in this study. These studies have clearly demonstrated the usefulness of the map of M'_{-1} (or potential) as an indication of the pattern of the distribution of many important areal variables.

H_γ can be generalized in the same way that MD_γ and S_C were generalized. The *general harmonic mean distance deviation* is denoted by H_P. For ungrouped data, $H_P = \dfrac{P}{\sum\limits_{X=1}^{P} (M'_{-1} \ at \ x)}$ while for grouped data, $H_P = \dfrac{P}{\sum\limits_{i=1}^{N} \left[p_i \ (M'_{-1} \ at \ i) \right]}$ where i again represents the control point of class i. Since $V_j = P(M'_{-1} \ at \ j)$ these expressions can also be written as $H_P = \dfrac{P^2}{\sum\limits_{x=1}^{P} (V_x)}$ and $H_P = \dfrac{P^2}{\sum\limits_{i=1}^{N} (p_i V_i)}$.

Stewart ([89], p. 52) has defined *demographic energy*, E, as $\frac{1}{2} \sum\limits_{x=1}^{P} (V_x)$. For grouped data, $E = \frac{1}{2} \sum\limits_{i=1}^{N} (p_i V_i)$. Like its physical counterpart, this energy has units of mass (numbers of items in the population) squared per distance. Warntz [115] has shown that E can be a valuable tool in the analysis of the historical development of a population. From the above formulas it is obvious that H_P and E are functionally related and $H_P = \dfrac{P^2}{2E}$. Thus, H_P also will be useful for analyzing the expansion of an areal population over time.

Another advantage of H_P is its stability compared to H_γ. Since H_P is independent of any particular reference point, it is not greatly influenced by the area of any single class. Large differences in class areas and locations will cause only minor changes in H_P. For this reason, H_P often is used in preference to H_γ.

H_P also can be used as part of another valuable measure. The *mean potential*, V_M, is equal to $\dfrac{P}{H_P}$. This can be expressed in several ways. For ungrouped data, $V_M = \dfrac{\sum\limits_{x=1}^{P} (V_x)}{P}$ and for grouped data, $V_M = \dfrac{\sum\limits_{i=1}^{N} (p_i V_i)}{P}$. Thus, $V_M = \dfrac{2E}{P}$. V_M is *not* a measure of dispersion. It indicates the average potential of population for an areal distribution, and V_M has the units of potential of population, population divided by distance. Since potential of population is so closely related to many socio-economic variables, V_M is the best single index of the socio-economic

---

15In this study, all potentials will be designated by V. Thus, potential of population can refer to population in a general, statistical sense as well as to human population.

growth of a human population over a period of time. An even better indication of economic development is provided by V_M when income is used as the population.

The ratio of H_P to H_γ is still another interesting measure. $H_P = \dfrac{P}{V_M}$ and $H_\gamma = \dfrac{P}{V_c}$, so $\dfrac{H_P}{H_\gamma} = \dfrac{V_c}{V_M}$. Therefore, this ratio can be described as the ratio of the peak value of potential of population to the mean value of potential of population. As such $\dfrac{H_P}{H_\gamma}$ measures the relative strength or dominance of the peak, H_c. When $\dfrac{H_P}{H_\gamma} > 2$, $V_c > 2V_M$ and the peak may be described as dominant. Unlike the corresponding ratios based on M_1' and M_2', $\dfrac{H_P}{H_\gamma}$ can have a wide range of values. Obviously this ratio cannot be less than one, but there is no finite upper limit. In practice the values of $\dfrac{H_P}{H_\gamma}$ usually vary only between 1 and 4.

There is another important relationship among measures of dispersion. For a given areal distribution, the magnitudes of the measures of dispersion based on areal moments must be in direct order of the number of the moments. In symbolic notation, $min. \sqrt[-n]{M'_{-n}} \leq \cdots \leq min. \sqrt[-1]{M'_{-1}} \leq min. \sqrt[1]{M'_1} \leq min. \sqrt{M'_2} \leq \cdots \leq min. \sqrt[n]{M'_n}$. For the three measures of dispersion previously introduced, $H_\gamma \leq MD_\gamma \leq S_\gamma$. This also holds for the general measures of dispersion, and, for a given distribution, $H_P \leq MD_P \leq S_P$.

Moreover, this relationship exists for areal moments computed about any specified position. Thus, for a given areal distribution, $\left[\sqrt[-n]{M'_{-n}} \; at \; j\right] \leq \cdots \leq \left[\sqrt[-1]{M'_{-1}} \; at \; j\right] \leq \left[\sqrt[1]{M'_1} \; at \; j\right] \leq \left[\sqrt{M'_2} \; at \; j\right] \leq \cdots \leq \left[\sqrt[n]{M'_n} \; at \; j\right]$. In particular $\sqrt[-n]{M_{-n}} \leq \cdots \leq \sqrt[-1]{M_{-1}} \leq \sqrt[1]{M_1} \leq \sqrt{M_2} \leq \cdots \leq \sqrt[n]{M_n}$. Using this relationship one can, on occasion, obtain surprisingly accurate estimates of M_n from a knowledge of M_{n-1} and M_{n+1}.

One point about this system of areal moments should be restated here. While the definition of areal moments is similar to that of ordinary statistical moments, the relative usefulness of individual areal moments is quite different from that of its linear counterparts. The second moment is all-important in linear statistics while the second areal moment has serious weaknesses for many types of problems.[16] Conversely, the linear inverse first moment is rarely used, while the areal inverse first moment is the most valuable of all the areal moments in many situations.

---

[16] See pp. 121–122.

Other Measures of Dispersion

Each one of the infinite number of areal moments has a measure of average position and a corresponding measure of dispersion. In addition to the measures previously mentioned a *third moment distance deviation*, III_γ, can be defined as the minimum value of $\sqrt[3]{M_3'}$ or the value of $\sqrt[3]{M_3'}$ at III_C. Similarly, the *fourth moment distance deviation*, IV_γ, would be the minimum value of $\sqrt[4]{M_4'}$ and the *inverse second moment distance deviation*, $-II_\gamma$, would be the minimum value of $\sqrt[-2]{M_{-2}'}$. However, these measures have the same shortcomings as their corresponding measures of average position and they are rarely used. Measures of dispersion based on M_n' when $n>4$ depend almost exclusively on extreme locations and are never used. In the opposite direction, measures based on M_n'' when $n<-2$ are never used because even moderately large distances have very little effect on the value of the parameter.

General measures of dispersion can easily be defined for all areal moments. However, since S_P, MD_P, and H_P are the only ones that are used and all the others possess many of the disadvantages of their corresponding measures of dispersion, no additional general measures of dispersion will be introduced in this study.

G_C also has a related measure of dispersion. The *geometric mean distance deviation*, G_γ, is the minimum value of the antilog of $\sum_{x=1}^{P} (log\ r_{jx})$ for ungrouped data and the minimum value of the antilog of $\sum_{i=1}^{N} (p_i\ log\ r_{ij})$ for grouped data. G_γ has the same defect as G_C; large differences in distances produce extremely small differences in the value of G_γ. Another disadvantage of G_γ is that a laborious computational procedure is needed to obtain its value. Chiefly because of these two factors, G_γ is seldom used. A general geometric mean distance deviation could be defined, but it would have no special advantages and it would require a tremendous amount of computation. Hence, such a measure would probably never be used, and so it will not be discussed here.

The easiest measure to understand and compute in linear statistics is the range. For areal distributions the *distance range*, W, is simply the greatest distance between any two members of the population. This parameter has little meaning since it depends on the location of only two items. In fact, W usually gives more important information about the area being considered than it does about the population. This property of W will be examined in more detail in Chapter VII. There are other minor measures of dispersion that are related to certain model surfaces. These will be discussed in Chapter VI.

Some Applications of Measures of Dispersion

The values of four measures of dispersion, W, MD_γ, S_γ, and H_γ, for the human populations of the seven countries that are being examined in this study are shown in *Table 4*.

TABLE 4

MEASURES OF DISPERSION FOR THE DISTRIBUTION
OF POPULATION IN SEVEN NATIONS

Nation	W (miles)	MD_γ (miles)	S_γ (miles)	H_γ (miles)
Australia	2480	440	615	75
United Kingdom	750	115	134	26
Brazil	2550	594	697	123
Japan	1420	213	256	66
United States	2900	667	839	146
India	1800	480	538	291
China	3070	495	579	253

If the entire population consisted of the two items that determine the value of W, then $MD_\gamma = S_\gamma = H_\gamma = \frac{W}{2}$. When items are located between the two extreme locations, $H_\gamma \le MD_\gamma \le S_\gamma \le \frac{W}{2}$. Thus, one-half the distance range serves as an upper limit for the values of the measures of dispersion.[17] From *Table 4* it can be seen that all the values presented there are considerably below this limit.

One of the most interesting features of these parameters is that most of the values of H_γ are very small. This indicates a great clustering of population about H_c, particularly in Australia, the United Kingdom, Brazil, Japan, and the United States. The only real exception to this observation is India which has the largest value of H_γ although four of the other nations have a larger area. This provides some quantitative evidence of the fact that the Indian harmonic mean center does not exert a very strong influence on the pattern of population. This was noted earlier when it was observed that the population of India was a bimodal distribution where H_c was not located at either the modal center (Calcutta) or the secondary modal center (Bombay).

---

[17] H_P, MD_P, and S_P have an upper limit of $\frac{W}{\sqrt{2}}$.

As stated previously $H_P \le MD_P \le S_P$ and $S_P \le \sqrt{2} S_\gamma$.

Therefore, $H_P \le MD_P \le S_P \le \sqrt{2} S_\gamma$.

But, $S_\gamma \le \frac{W}{2}$.

Therefore, $H_P \le MD_P \le S_P \le \frac{W}{\sqrt{2}}$.

Another feature that deserves mention is that the highest values of MD_γ and S_γ occur in the United States although Australia, Brazil, and China have as large or larger areas. These parameters demonstrate that the population in the United States is dispersed over most of the area of the country, while Australia, Brazil and China have large uninhabited regions in the part of the nation furthest from the average position.

The general measures of dispersion, MD_P, S_P, and H_P for these countries are presented in *Table 5*. Also shown here are V_M and the ratio of H_P to H_γ.

TABLE 5

GENERAL MEASURES OF DISPERSION FOR THE DISTRIBUTIONS
OF POPULATION IN SEVEN NATIONS

Nation	MD_P (miles)	$S_P{}^*$ (miles)	H_P (miles)	$\dfrac{H_P}{H_\gamma}$	V_M (thousands, persons per mile)
Australia	634	870	106	1.41	72
United Kingdom	163	190	69	2.64	725
Brazil	826	986	289	2.35	180
Japan	305	362	121	1.84	735
United States	954	1187	370	2.54	482
India	669	760	351	1.21	1113
China	703	819	378	1.49	1692

*S_p calculated from the relationship, $S_p = \sqrt{2}S_\gamma$.

Three of the nations, the United Kingdom, the United States, and Brazil, can be considered to have "strong" or "dominant" peaks of potential since the ratio of V_c to V_M $\left(\text{or } \dfrac{H_P}{H_\gamma}\right)$ is greater than two. This ratio also provides more evidence of the weakness of the Indian harmonic mean center. China also has a relatively weak peak of potential since the population is well scattered throughout the eastern part of the country. The most unusual case is Australia. There, most of the population is concentrated into a very small area along the southeastern coast from Brisbane to Adelaide. Such a situation is usually associated with a dominant peak of potential and a very large value of $\dfrac{H_P}{H_\gamma}$. However, this has not happened in

Australia. In fact, the potential of population at Sydney is only slightly higher than the value at Melbourne and the ratio of H_P to H_γ is considerably less than two.

The patterns of potential of population can be seen by examining both the values of V_M given in *Table 5* and the maps showing the distributions of potential for these countries *(Figures 16-22)*.

The most important feature of these maps is the area where the potential is greater than V_M. This area, however small, dominates the socio-economic life of the nation. In Australia this area consisted of only the cities of Sydney and Melbourne and their immediate environs. For the United Kingdom this area was a larger portion of the total area and consisted of two regions which almost formed a ridge between London and Liverpool.

The case of Brazil was similar to that of Australia. There was a small ridge of high potential between the two major cities, Rio de Janeiro and Sao Paulo. In addition, Brazil had a subsidiary peak at Recife. Japan, in turn, had a distribution that resembled the pattern of the United Kingdom. V_M bounded a region in Japan that was an almost continuous ridge from the harmonic mean center at Tokyo to the subsidiary peak at Osaka. The corresponding ridge in the United States extended from New York City to Chicago. This region includes one of the greatest concentrations of people, industry, business, and wealth in the world.

In India, the potential was greater than V_M in the Ganges river valley from Delhi to Calcutta. There were also separate subsidiary peaks at Hyderabad and Madras. The largest of all of these high potential regions was found in China. This was a triangularly shaped ridge that extended from Shanghai northward to Peiping and westward to Chungking. Within this region is the world's greatest concentration of population. In 1957 there were approximately 350,000,000 people in this region whose area is 20 percent smaller than Alaska.

The distributions of the mean convergence distance, M_1', for these seven nations are shown in *Figures 23-29*. The values on these maps represent the average distance to all the members of the population. From these maps it is easy to see how these isolines start as ellipses near MD_c but rapidly approach a series of concentric circles as the distance from MD_c increases.

These values are useful tools in problems involving the selection of optimum locations. For example, assume that a man has the task of selecting a site for a convention of a large organization composed of people living in the United States. Let us further assume that he has received only three suitable offers and these have come from Boston, Chicago, and Los Angeles. Let us also assume that some preliminary analysis has revealed that the distribution of the membership of the organization is very similar to the areal distribution of the United States population in 1960. Then, by referring to *Figure 27*, he can see that the members of his organization would have to fly approximately 700 miles, on the average, to reach Chicago. The corresponding figures for Boston and Los Angeles would be 1000 miles and 1900 miles, respectively. These differences would undoubtedly have an effect on the final decision. Of course, this example is an over-simplification. However, it does indicate the type of problem where the values of M_1' can provide useful, quantitative information.

The values of some measures of dispersion, V_M, and the ratio of H_P to H_γ for the history of the United States population are shown in *Tables 6* and *7*. The graph of the values of S_γ, MD_γ, H_γ, S_P, MD_P, and H_P from 1754 to 1960 appears as *Figure 30*.

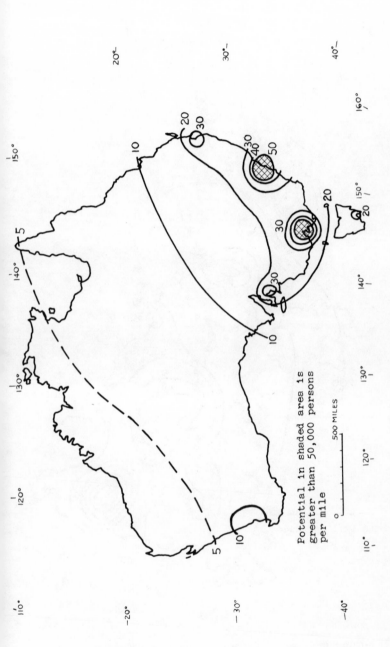

Potential in shaded area is
greater than 50,000 persons
per mile

500 MILES

FIGURE 16. — Potential of Population - Australia, 1947 (thousands, persons per mile)

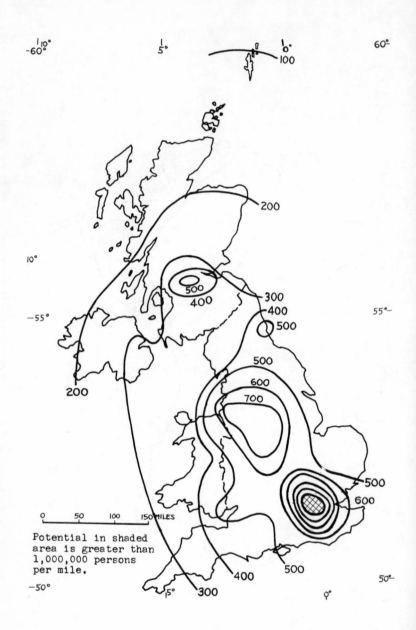

FIGURE 17.—Potential of Population - United Kingdom, 1951
(thousands, persons per mile)

FIGURE 18.—Potential of Population - Brazil, 1950
(thousands, persons per mile)

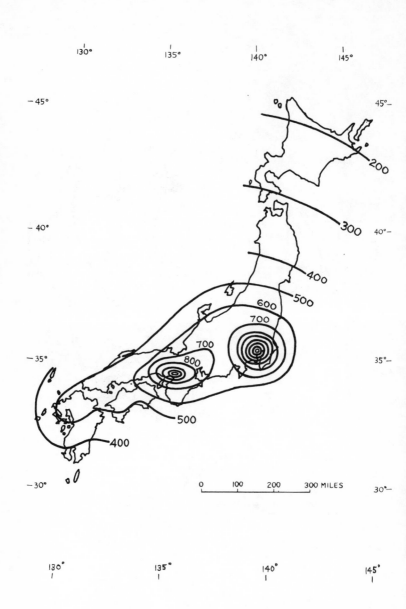

FIGURE 19.—Potential of Population - Japan, 1955
(thousands, persons per mile)

73

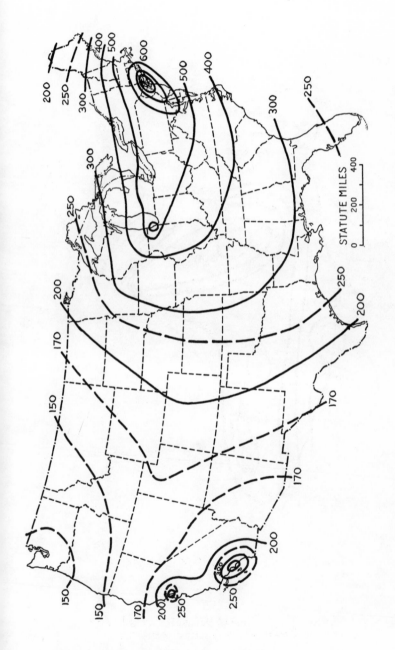

FIGURE 20. – Potential of Population – United States, 1960 (thousands, persons per mile)

74

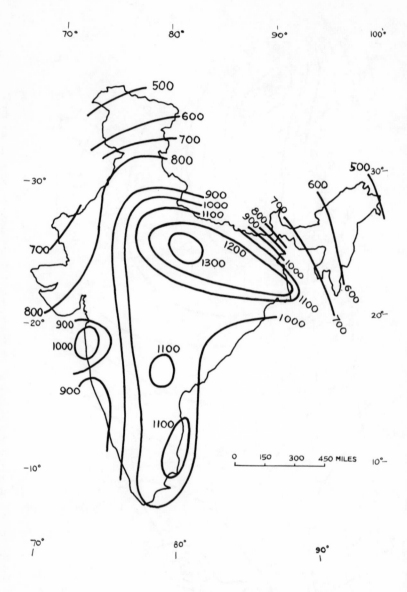

FIGURE 21.—Potential of Population - India, 1957
(thousands, persons per mile)

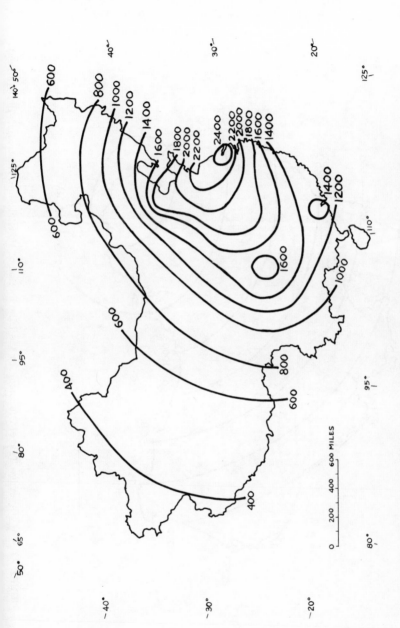

FIGURE 22. — Potential of Population – China, 1957 (thousands, persons per mile)

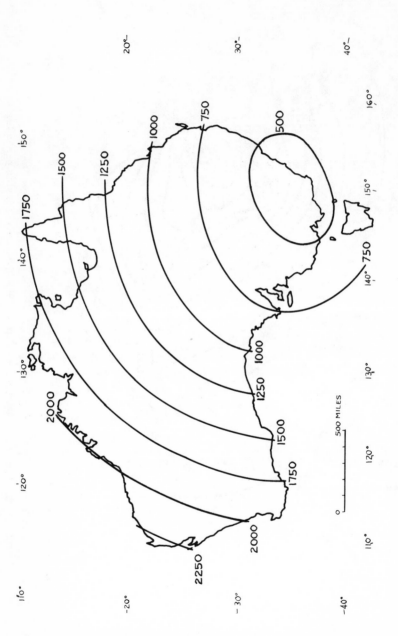

FIGURE 23. — M_i^i (Average Travel Distance) for the Distribution of Population in Australia, 1947 (miles)

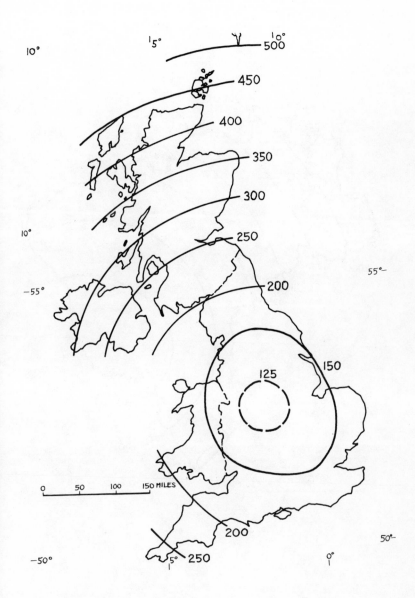

FIGURE 24. — M'_i (Average Travel Distance) for the Distribution of
Population in the United Kingdom, 1951 (miles)

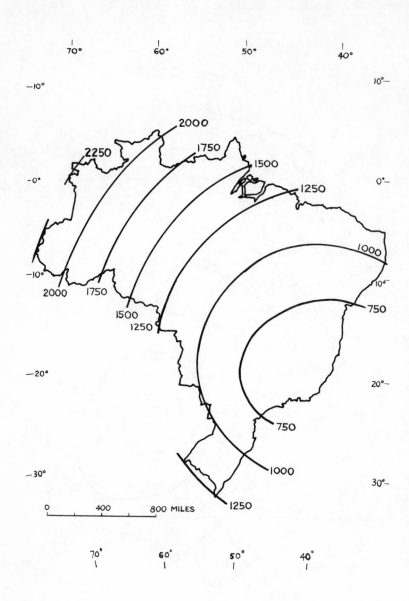

FIGURE 25.—M_i' (Average Travel Distance) for the Distribution of
Population in Brazil, 1950 (miles)

79

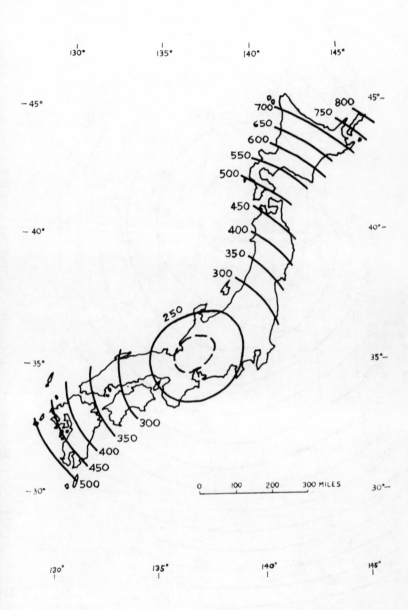

FIGURE 26. — M'_i (Average Travel Distance) for the Distribution of
Population in Japan, 1955 (miles)

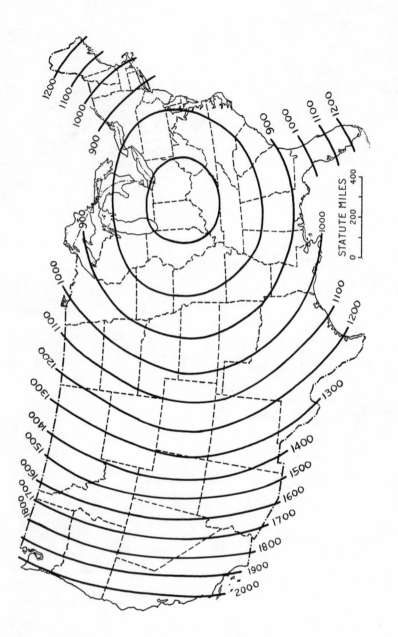

FIGURE 27. — M_i' (Average Travel Distance) for the Distribution of Population in the United States, 1960 (miles)

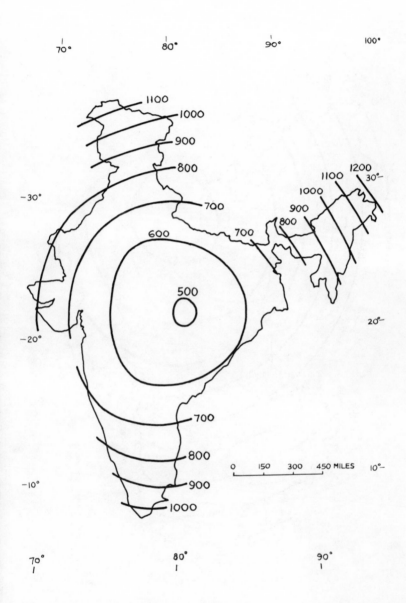

FIGURE 28. — M_i' (Average Travel Distance) for the Distribution of Population in India, 1957 (miles)

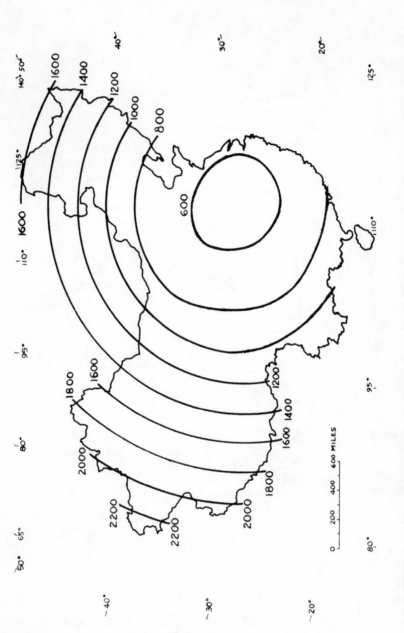

FIGURE 29. — M_i (Average Travel Distance) for the Distribution of Population in China, 1957 (miles)

TABLE 6

MEASURES OF DISPERSION FOR THE DISTRIBUTION OF
POPULATION IN THE UNITED STATES, 1754-1960

Date	W (miles)	MD_γ (miles)	S_γ (miles)	H_γ (miles)
1754	1260	205	240	84
1775	1280	224	262	104
1790	1300	227	281	116
1800	1670	238	303	119
1810	1770	265	339	130
1820	1800	301	365	140
1830	1810	326	384	149
1840	1810	356	403	155
1850	2900	389	462	157
1860	2900	433	527	154
1870	2900	448	550	155
1880	2900	480	585	163
1890	2900	510	623	165
1900	2900	528	639	158
1910	2900	558	685	148
1920	2900	574	705	145
1930	2900	584	736	138
1940	2900	593	755	138
1950	2900	630	802	142
1960	2900	667	839	146

TABLE 7

GENERAL MEASURES OF DISPERSION FOR THE POPULATION
OF THE UNITED STATES, 1754-1960

Date	MD_P (miles)	$S_P{}^*$ (miles)	H_P (miles)	$\dfrac{H_P}{H_\gamma}$	V_M (thousands, persons per mile)
1754	291	339	116	1.38	12
1775	317	370	138	1.33	18
1790	321	397	172	1.48	23
1800	337	429	191	1.61	28
1810	376	480	213	1.64	34
1820	428	516	236	1.69	41
1830	461	543	247	1.66	52
1840	504	570	270	1.74	63
1850	562	653	288	1.83	81

TABLE 7--Continued

Date	MD_P (miles)	S_P* (miles)	H_P (miles)	$\dfrac{H_P}{H_\gamma}$	V_M (thousands, persons per mile)
1860	628	745	313	2.03	100
1870	650	777	323	2.09	120
1880	694	827	345	2.11	146
1890	736	881	364	2.21	173
1900	761	904	368	2.33	207
1910	803	969	379	2.56	243
1920	825	997	381	2.63	277
1930	840	1041	384	2.78	320
1940	852	1068	389	2.82	339
1950	903	1134	400	2.82	377
1960	954	1187	370	2.54	482

*S_p calculated from the relationship, $S_p = \sqrt{2} S_\gamma$

The history of these parameters can now be examined within the framework of the four periods of American demographic history based on the rate of movement of S_c. From 1754 to 1790, S_c moved slowly as the population remained near the east coast. However, the population was spreading out along the coast as evidenced by increasing values of S_γ, MD_γ, H_γ and their corresponding general measures of dispersion. Only two small areas, near Boston and Baltimore, had values of potential that were greater than V_M. H_c shifted from Boston to Philadelphia during this period but neither was a dominant peak of potential as $\dfrac{H_P}{H_\gamma}$ remained less than 1.5.

The century between 1790 and 1890 should be subdivided into two periods. The time from 1790 through 1830 was the first phase of the mass movement into the interior portion of the continent. The values of S_γ and MD_γ increased rapidly. H_γ also increased, but more slowly, as the urban commercial centers of the northeast began to emerge. By 1830 the harmonic mean center had moved to its present location at New York City although this was still a relatively "weak" peak $\left(\dfrac{H_P}{H_\gamma} = 1.66\right)$. In the 1790's the region where potential was greater than V_M became a ridge near the east coast extending from north of Boston to Richmond. Gradually this ridge began to expand toward the west and, by 1830, this region also extended from New York City to the Ohio river valley in eastern Ohio.

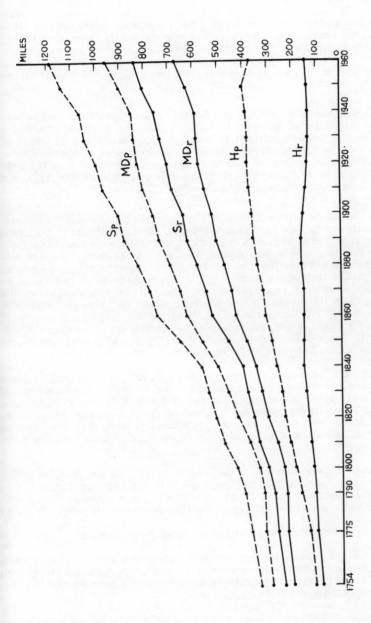

FIGURE 30. — Measures of Dispersion and General Measures of Dispersion for the Distribution of Population in the United States, 1754-1960

From 1830 to 1890 westward migration was the primary demographic feature in the United States. S_c and MD_c continued to move westward at a rapid pace. Of course, this caused similar large increases in the values of S_γ and MD_γ. However, the absolute increase in population was also very large in the vicinity of New York, with the result that the value of H_γ was only 11 percent larger in 1890 than it was in 1830. This corresponds to increases of 62 percent in S_γ and S_P, 56 percent in MD_γ, and 60 percent in MD_P. Even H_P increased by 47 percent during this period.

This sharpening of the peak of potential at New York City is further indicated by the fact that the ratio of H_P to H_γ rose from 1.66 in 1830 to 2.21 in 1890. The region where potential exceeded V_M continued to expand toward the west. As railroad track replaced water as the primary route for the transportation of freight, the western end of this ridge shifted northward from the cities on the Ohio river to Chicago. By 1890 this region had a triangular shape, with vertices near Boston, Richmond, and Chicago.

The outstanding feature of the period between 1890 and 1940 was the increasing dominance of the New York peak of potential. This is indicated by the rise of the ratio of H_P to H_γ from 2.21 in 1890 to 2.82 in 1940. Moreover, the value of H_γ was declining during this period, with a net decrease of 16 percent in 50 years. This is more evidence of increasing concentration of population in the eastern part of the country during the first part of the twentieth century. At the same time, westward expansion became much slower with the closing of the frontier. From 1890 to 1940, S_c moved westward at a very slow pace while MD_c hardly moved at all. During this period the values of S_γ and S_P increased by 27 percent, the values of MD_γ and MD_P rose 16 percent, and H_P increased by only 7 percent. The region where potential of population was greater than V_M remained the same, its boundaries being virtually constant for 50 years.

Since 1940 the pattern has changed again. In this case, the primary factor was the rapid growth of population along the west coast. The San Francisco and Los Angeles areas emerged as strong, although still secondary, peaks of potential. The westward movement of S_c was accelerated because of the extreme location of the west coast, while MD_c continued to remain in one small area. Changes in the values of S_γ and MD_γ also were slightly accelerated during this period.

Another important trend in the 1940's and 1950's was the movement to suburbia and the formation of the "megalopolis" in the northeast. In this 20 year period the population around and between the large cities increased more rapidly than the population within the limits of these cities. Therefore, New York City became somewhat less dominant as shown by the fact that $\dfrac{H_P}{H_\gamma}$ fell to 2.50 in 1960 and H_γ began to increase again after 1940. However, the region of greater than mean potential continued to be the Boston-Richmond-Chicago triangle, although the relative importance of this region has been diminished by the emergence of the west coast peak.

In spite of these differences among various periods, the one basic overall feature is that the dispersion of the population of the United States has been

increasing throughout its history. Evidence of this is given by the almost continually increasing values of S_P, MD_P, and H_P. Another way of showing this
effect is presented in *Figure 31*. Here, the values of P and V_M are plotted on a
semi-logarithmic grid. Thus, the slope of each curve represents the variable's
rate of change. If the areal pattern of the population had not changed, the curves
of both P and V_M would have the same slope. The fact that P has increased at a
faster rate than V_M indicates that the population has become more dispersed.

In the preceding section, various measures of dispersion have been used to
provide quantitative indications of areal demographic patterns and trends over a
period of time. These measures also were used to compare distributions for
several areas at one time. In this latter case, these measures have one severe
limitation. While areal measures of dispersion are theoretically comparable
because they all are in units of distance, their values are greatly influenced by
the size of the areas involved. It is certainly not surprising that S_y is greater
for the distribution of people in China than it is for the similar distribution within
the United Kingdom.

However, areal measures of dispersion can easily be related to the size of
the area to form a *measure of relative dispersion*. The values of these measures
for various areas can be compared to give a meaningful indication of the patterns
of dispersion within the areas. While it may be useful to compare areal distributions with each other, some definite theoretical standard is desirable as a basis
for comparison. For example, the normal curve is a standard for linear distributions. Certain mathematical models of surfaces can be developed to serve a
similar purpose for areal distributions. Then, the values of the measures of
relative dispersion for these model surfaces can be used as a basis for comparison of similar parameters of actual areal populations. In this way the usefulness of areal measures of dispersion can be significantly increased. Therefore,
the discussion of dispersion will be interrupted for one chapter to permit the
introduction of these model surfaces. Following this, the measures of relative
dispersion will be developed in Chapter VII.

88

P (in millions of persons)

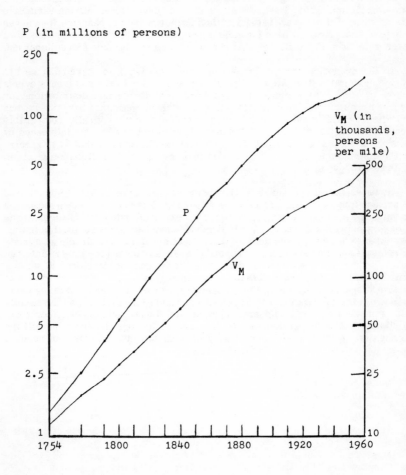

FIGURE 31. —P and V_M for the Distribution of Population
in the United States, 1754-1960

CHAPTER VI
MODEL SURFACES

The Normal Probability Surface

One of the most valuable tools of linear statistics is the normal curve of error. Its importance in Probability Theory, Sampling Theory, and as a theoretical distribution with which actual distributions can be compared, has received extensive attention in statistical literature. It is not necessary to repeat these discussions here.

The normal curve is a linear distribution of one variable. In any specific instance, it is defined by three parameters—the mean and the standard deviation of the distribution and the total number of observations. Mathematical statisticians have applied the concept of the normal curve to distributions of more than one variable. In the case of two variables, this model has been called the bivariate normal distribution or the normal correlation surface. When there is no correlation between the two variables and the standard deviations are equal $(\sigma_x = \sigma_y)$, the bivariate normal distribution is simply the surface of revolution of the normal curve.

This special case of the bivariate normal has been called the *surface of probability*.[1] Since an areal distribution can be regarded as a bivariate distribution, the surface of probability can obviously be used in the study of areal distributions. Such an application was first made by Johnson ([56], pp. 38-47) in 1892 when he used this model in discussing the distribution of bullet marks in target practice.

While the surface of probability can be a valuable tool in the analysis of areal distributions, it has two disadvantages. The first of these is that the bivariate approach does not consider the sphericity of the earth since the standard deviation of the distribution is based on the Pythagorean Theorem $\left(\sigma = \sqrt{\dfrac{\sigma_x^2 + \sigma_y^2}{2}} \right)$. Of course, this factor is important only when a very large area is being considered. The surface of probability also is a rather complicated model to use. While its form does not depend on the choice of a particular coordinate system, a pair of orthogonal axes must be established so that the means and standard deviations of the two variables can be computed. The necessity of calculating both σ_x and σ_y also adds to the amount of labor needed when the bivariate model is employed.

These difficulties, although usually relatively minor, can easily be overcome by basing a probability surface on the standard distance deviation. This model

---

[1]Johnson [56], p. 40.

will be called the *Normal Probability Surface* and it is defined by three parameters, P, S_c, and S_r. Its equation is $D_x = \dfrac{P}{S_r^2} e^{-r^2/S_r^2}$ where D_x is the density at a distance, $\dfrac{r}{S_r}$, from S_c. Of course, density at a point is ambiguous, but it is a useful mathematical abstraction:

> "It is intended that this density function measure the number of items of the population in a unit of area centered on a point when this unit area is a square with side equal to one unit of distance. It is also required that the population be large enough and that the units of area be small in relation to the total area so that the density distribution may be regarded as a continuous surface."[2]

The maximum, or central, density of this model, D_c, occurs at S_c and $D_c = \dfrac{P}{S_r^2}$. Thus, $D_x = D_c e^{-r^2/S_r^2}$.

Densities for the Normal Probability Surface are shown in *Table 8*. This table is entered with the value of the distance from the arithmetic mean center divided by the standard distance deviation, $\dfrac{r}{S_r}$. The densities are stated as decimal fractions of the central density. Thus, the tabulated values represent $\dfrac{D_x}{D_c}$.

Volumes under the Normal Probability Surface are shown in *Table 9*. For an areal population that is distributed in accordance with this model, a value in *Table 9* represents the probability of an item of that population being located inside a circle with S_c as origin and having a radius of the value of $\dfrac{r}{S_r}$ corresponding to the value of volume in the table. Although this is a probability model, it may be considered as representing an areally distributed population by regarding the total population as certainty and by equating the total volume under the surface with the total population. Thus, if P_x is the population between S_c and $\dfrac{r}{S_r}$, the values in *Table 9* represent $\dfrac{P_x}{P}$.

One of the most interesting features of these tables is that, at any given distance $\dfrac{r}{S_r}$, the values in the two tables are complementary, that is $\dfrac{P_x}{P} = 1 - \dfrac{D_x}{D_c}$. This relationship is proven in *Appendix C*.

In the case when the areal base of the distribution is a section of a plane rather than of a sphere, the Normal Probability Surface is simply a bivariate

---

[2]Warntz and Neft [119], p. 56.

TABLE 8

DENSITIES OF THE NORMAL PROBABILITY SURFACE

At Distances $\frac{r}{S_r}$ from the Arithmetic Mean

Center, Expressed as Decimal Fractions

of the Maximum Central Density D_c

$\frac{r}{S_r}$	.00	.01	.02	.03	.04	.05	.06	.07	.08	.09
0.0	1.00000	.99990	.99960	.99910	.99840	.99750	.99640	.99511	.99362	.99193
0.1	.99005	.98797	.98570	.98324	.98059	.97775	.97472	.97151	.96812	.96454
0.2	.96079	.95686	.95275	.94848	.94403	.93941	.93463	.92969	.92459	.91934
0.3	.91393	.90837	.90267	.89682	.89083	.88471	.87845	.87206	.86554	.85890
0.4	.85214	.84527	.83828	.83119	.82399	.81669	.80929	.80180	.79422	.78655
0.5	.77880	.77097	.76307	.75510	.74707	.73897	.73081	.72260	.71434	.70603
0.6	.69768	.68929	.68068	.67240	.66392	.65541	.64686	.63833	.62977	.62120
0.7	.61263	.60405	.59547	.58690	.57834	.56978	.56124	.55272	.54422	.53574
0.8	.52729	.51886	.51048	.50211	.49381	.48554	.47730	.46912	.46098	.45289
0.9	.44486	.43688	.42896	.42109	.41329	.40555	.39788	.39028	.38274	.37527
1.0	.36788	.36056	.35331	.34614	.33905	.33204	.32511	.31825	.31149	.30480
1.1	.29820	.29168	.28525	.27890	.27264	.26647	.26038	.25439	.24848	.24266
1.2	.23693	.23129	.22573	.22027	.21490	.20961	.20446	.19931	.19429	.18936
1.3	.18452	.17977	.17510	.17052	.16603	.16162	.15730	.15306	.14891	.14484
1.4	.14086	.13696	.13313	.12939	.12573	.12215	.11865	.11522	.11187	.10860
1.5	.10540	.10227	.09922	.09624	.09333	.09049	.08772	.08502	.08238	.07981
1.6	.07730	.07486	.07248	.07017	.06791	.06571	.06357	.06149	.05946	.05749
1.7	.05558	.05371	.05190	.05014	.04843	.04677	.04516	.04359	.04207	.04060
1.8	.03916	.03778	.03643	.03512	.03386	.03263	.03144	.03029	.02918	.02810
1.9	.02705	.02604	.02506	.02412	.02320	.02231	.02146	.02063	.01983	.01906

TABLE 8--Continued

$\frac{x}{S_r}$	.00	.01	.02	.03	.04	.05	.06	.07	.08	.09
2.0	.01832	.01760	.01690	.01632	.01558	.01496	.01436	.01378	.01322	.01268
2.1	.01216	.01165	.01117	.01071	.01026	.00983	.00941	.00901	.00863	.00826
2.2	.00791	.00757	.00724	.00692	.00662	.00633	.00605	.00578	.00553	.00528
2.3	.00504	.00481	.00460	.00439	.00419	.00400	.00381	.00364	.00347	.00331
2.4	.00315	.00300	.00286	.00273	.00260	.00247	.00235	.00224	.00213	.00203
2.5	.00193	.00184	.00175	.00166	.00158	.00150	.00143	.00135	.00129	.00122
2.6	.00116	.00110	.00104	.00099	.00094	.00089	.00085	.00080	.00076	.00072
2.7	.00068	.00065	.00061	.00058	.00055	.00052	.00049	.00047	.00044	.00042
2.8	.00039	.00037	.00035	.00033	.00031	.00030	.00028	.00026	.00025	.00024
2.9	.00022	.00021	.00020	.00019	.00018	.00017	.00016	.00015	.00014	.00013
3.0	.00012	.00012	.00011	.00010	.00010	.00009	.00009	.00008	.00008	.00007
3.1	.00007	.00006	.00006	.00006	.00005	.00005	.00005	.00004	.00004	.00004
3.2	.00004	.00003	.00003	.00003	.00003	.00003	.00002	.00002	.00002	.00002
3.3	.00002	.00002	.00002	.00002	.00001	.00001	.00001	.00001	.00001	.00001
3.4	.00001	.00001	.00001	.00001	.00001	.00001	.00001	.00001	.00001	.00001
3.5	.00000*									

*This value approaches but never actually reaches zero. It is shown here as such only because the values in this table are rounded to five decimal places.

TABLE 9

VOLUMES UNDER THE NORMAL PROBABILITY SURFACE

Population Included Within a Circle Having

Radius $\frac{r}{S_r}$ with the Arithmetic Mean Center

as Origin, Expressed as a Decimal
Fraction of the Total Population

$\frac{r}{S_r}$	.00	.01	.02	.03	.04	.05	.06	.07	.08	.09
0.0	.00000	.00010	.00040	.00090	.00160	.00250	.00360	.00489	.00638	.00807
0.1	.00995	.01203	.01430	.01676	.01941	.02225	.02528	.02849	.03188	.03546
0.2	.03921	.04314	.04725	.05152	.05597	.06059	.06537	.07031	.07541	.08066
0.3	.08607	.09163	.09733	.10318	.10917	.11529	.12155	.12794	.13446	.14110
0.4	.14786	.15473	.16172	.16881	.17601	.18331	.19071	.19820	.20578	.21345
0.5	.22120	.22903	.23693	.24490	.25293	.26103	.26919	.27740	.28566	.29397
0.6	.30232	.31071	.31914	.32760	.33608	.34459	.35314	.36167	.37023	.37880
0.7	.38737	.39595	.40453	.41310	.42166	.43022	.43876	.44728	.45578	.46426
0.8	.47271	.48114	.48952	.49789	.50619	.51446	.52270	.53088	.53902	.54711
0.9	.55514	.56312	.57104	.57891	.58671	.59445	.60212	.60972	.61726	.62473
1.0	.63212	.63944	.64669	.65386	.66095	.66796	.67489	.68175	.68851	.69520
1.1	.70180	.70832	.71475	.72110	.72736	.73353	.73962	.74561	.75152	.75734
1.2	.76307	.76871	.77427	.77973	.78510	.79039	.79554	.80069	.80571	.81064
1.3	.81548	.82023	.82490	.82948	.83397	.83838	.84270	.84694	.85109	.85516
1.4	.85914	.86304	.86687	.87061	.87427	.87785	.88135	.88478	.88813	.89140

TABLE 9--Continued

$\frac{r}{s_r}$	.00	.01	.02	.03	.04	.05	.06	.07	.08	.09
1.5	.89460	.89773	.90078	.90376	.90667	.90951	.91228	.91498	.91762	.92019
1.6	.92270	.92514	.92752	.92983	.93209	.93429	.93643	.93851	.94054	.94251
1.7	.94442	.94629	.94810	.94986	.95157	.95323	.95484	.95641	.95793	.95940
1.8	.96084	.96222	.96357	.96488	.96614	.96737	.96856	.96971	.97082	.97190
1.9	.97295	.97396	.97494	.97588	.97680	.97769	.97854	.97937	.98017	.98094
2.0	.98168	.98240	.98310	.98377	.98442	.98504	.98564	.98622	.98678	.98732
2.1	.98784	.98835	.98883	.98929	.98974	.99017	.99059	.99099	.99137	.99174
2.2	.99209	.99243	.99276	.99308	.99338	.99367	.99395	.99422	.99447	.99472
2.3	.99496	.99519	.99540	.99561	.99581	.99600	.99619	.99636	.99653	.99669
2.4	.99685	.99700	.99714	.99727	.99740	.99753	.99765	.99776	.99787	.99797
2.5	.99807	.99816	.99825	.99834	.99842	.99850	.99857	.99865	.99871	.99878
2.6	.99884	.99890	.99896	.99901	.99906	.99911	.99915	.99920	.99924	.99928
2.7	.99932	.99935	.99939	.99942	.99945	.99948	.99951	.99953	.99956	.99958
2.8	.99961	.99963	.99965	.99967	.99969	.99970	.99972	.99974	.99975	.99976
2.9	.99978	.99979	.99980	.99981	.99982	.99983	.99984	.99985	.99986	.99987
3.0	.99988	.99988	.99989	.99990	.99990	.99991	.99991	.99992	.99992	.99993
3.1	.99993	.99994	.99994	.99994	.99995	.99995	.99995	.99996	.99996	.99996
3.2	.99996	.99997	.99997	.99997	.99997	.99997	.99998	.99998	.99998	.99998
3.3	.99998	.99998	.99998	.99998	.99999	.99999	.99999	.99999	.99999	.99999
3.4	.99999	.99999	.99999	.99999	.99999	.99999	.99999	.99999	.99999	.99999
3.5	1.00000*									

*This value approaches but never actually equals one. It is shown here as such only because the values in this table are rounded to five decimal places.

normal distribution with variances $\dfrac{S_r^2}{2}$ and $\dfrac{S_r^2}{2}$ and with zero correlation between the two variables. This relationship may be more easily seen when the equation of the Normal Probability Surface is expressed in the following form:

$$\text{Probability } \left(\frac{r}{S_r} \leq \propto\right) = 1 - e^{-\propto^2}$$

This also reveals additional relationships between the Normal Probability Surface and other distributions such as the chi-square (χ^2). For a chi-square distribution with two degrees of freedom:

$$\text{Probability } (\chi \leq \propto) = 1 - e^{-\frac{\propto^2}{2}}$$

From the last two equations it can be seen that the distribution of $\dfrac{2r^2}{S_r^2}$ has the form of χ^2 with two degrees of freedom.

It now becomes necessary to distinguish between two related, but distinct, definitions of the term "density". D_x represents the familiar areal density, the number of items of the population in a unit of area. In addition, the mathematical concept of *probability density* can also be applied to areal distributions. The areal probability density function defines the relative number of items of a population within a ring of a given elementary width, dr (the elementary annulus). The probability density function is related to the areal density function with $P=1$ by a factor equal to the circumference of the annulus. Thus, if the probability density function be denoted by PD_x, then $PD_x = 2\pi r Dx$. For the Normal Probability Surface:[3]

$$PD_x = 2\pi r \left(\frac{1}{\pi S_r^2} e^{-r^2/S_r^2}\right) = \frac{2r}{S_r^2} e^{-r^2/S_r^2}.$$

The maximum value of this function indicates the location of the elementary annulus which contains the greatest number of items of the population. For this surface this maximum occurs at a distance equal to $\dfrac{S_r}{\sqrt{2}}$ from S_c. This distance has been called the *most probable distance*, PD_r, and it is a measure of areal dispersion for a Normal Probability Surface distribution.[4]

Additional measures of dispersion can be derived from the values in *Table 9*. The radius of a circle with origin S_c that includes a certain proportion of the population can be considered to be a measure of dispersion of that population. When this proportion is *1/2*, the measure is usually called the *probable error*.

---

[3]In Warntz and Neft [119] the Normal Probability Surface was called the Probability Density Surface. The name was changed here to avoid confusion between this particular model and the infinite number of possible probability density functions.

[4]Johnson [56], pp. 43–44.

For areal distributions the probable error will be designated by the symbol PE_r. In the case of the Normal Probability Surface $PE_r = \sqrt{log_e 2} S_r = 0.8326 S_r$.

PE_r is not the only measure of dispersion that can be derived from *Table 9*. Radii of circles with origin at S_c including any proportion of the population indicate dispersion. Measures of this type will be designated by PC_{ru} where "u" is the percentage of the population included within the circle$\left(u = \dfrac{P_x[100]}{P} \right)$. Thus, a whole series of these *percentile distance deviations* for the Normal Probability Surface can be defined and their values interpolated from the values in *Table 9*. For example, $PC_{r10} = 0.3246 S_r$, $PC_{r25} = 0.5364 S_r$, $PC_{r75} = 1.1774 S_r$, and $PC_{r90} = 1.5174 S_r$. Of course, $PC_{r50} = PE_r$. Due to the relationships mentioned earlier, these values also can be computed from a table of probabilities of the chi-square distribution. The relationship can be expressed as follows:

$$2(PC_{ru})^2 = \chi^2$$ with *2* degrees of freedom where the probability of a value of χ^2 equal to or greater than the given value is $\dfrac{u}{100}$.

There are three basic ways in which the Normal Probability Surface is used. First, it is a model of an areal distribution to which actual distributions can be compared. This is usually done by comparing the percentage of the population within a certain number of standard distance deviations from S_c for the actual distribution with the corresponding value for this model.

The Normal Probability Surface also provides a series of standard values for various measures of relative dispersion, skewness, kurtosis, etc. These values also can be used to compare actual distributions with the Normal Probability Surface.

Finally, this model is very important in Areal Sampling Theory. Like its counterpart in linear statistics, the Normal Curve, it is a distribution of errors and many sampling distributions are closely related to the Normal Probability Surface. These applications of the Normal Probability Surface will be illustrated later in this chapter and in subsequent chapters.

Uniform Distributions

Uniform, or even, distributions are surfaces where the density for each unit area within the total area being studied is the same $\left(D_x = D_c = \dfrac{P}{A} \right)$. The properties of such a distribution depend on the shape of the total area. Thus, there are an infinite number of possible model surfaces of even distributions. For the sake of simplicity and uniformity, the only even distribution that will be used as a model surface in this study is the *Circular Uniform Surface* where the total area is assumed to have the shape of a circle with radius "r".

Now the density can be defined as a function of r: $D_x = \dfrac{P}{A} = \dfrac{P}{\pi r^2}$. If r_x represents the distance from the origin to location x, the circumference of an elementary annulus is equal to $2\pi r_x$. Thus, when $P=1$, $PD_x = 2\pi r_x D_x = 2\pi r_x\left(\dfrac{1}{\pi r^2}\right) = \dfrac{2r_x}{r^2}$, and $PD_r = r$. For this model $S_r = \dfrac{r}{\sqrt{2}}$ so $PD_r = \sqrt{2}S_r$. The expression for the volume under the Circular Uniform Surface is $\dfrac{P_x}{P} = \dfrac{r_x^2}{r^2}$. Therefore, $PC_{ru} = \sqrt[3]{\dfrac{u}{100}}r = \sqrt{\dfrac{u}{50}}S_r$, $PE_r = \dfrac{r}{\sqrt{2}} = S_r$, $PC_{r25} = \dfrac{r}{2} = \dfrac{S_r}{\sqrt{2}}$, etc.

The Circular Uniform Surface has two of the same basic uses as the Normal Probability Surface. The lone exception is that the Circular Uniform Surface is not important in Areal Sampling Theory. Since the surface of this model is always parallel to the surface of the sphere, the Circular Uniform Surface is often employed as a standard, indicating the minimum degree of concentration about the average positions. Parameters of actual areal distributions can then be compared to this standard.

The Mean Deviation Surface

Several social scientists have proposed models for the distributions of individuals within an urban area. Most of these are based on empirical evidence and are limited to this type of application.[5] Recently, Taitel [100] has suggested an exponential model which could be applied to other types of areal distributions. Since the dispersion parameter of this model is MD_r, it will be referred to as the *Mean Deviation Surface*. Its density function is $D_x = \dfrac{2P}{\pi\left(MD_r\right)^2}e^{-\frac{2r}{MD_r}}$ where D_x is the density at a distance, $\dfrac{r}{MD_r}$, from MD_c, and $D_c = \dfrac{2P}{\pi\left(MD_r\right)^2}$. Density and volume tables for the surface (similar to *Tables 8* and *9* for the Normal Probability Surface) are shown as *Tables 10* and *11*.

When $P=1$, $PD_x = 2\pi r D_x = 2\pi r\left[\dfrac{2}{\pi\left(MD_r\right)^2}\right]e^{-\frac{2r}{MD_r}} = \dfrac{4r}{\left(MD_r\right)^2}e^{-\frac{2r}{MD_r}}$. This probability density function reaches its maximum at $\dfrac{r}{MD_r} = \dfrac{1}{2}$ so $PD_r = \dfrac{MD_r}{2}$. Moreover, $MD_r = \sqrt{\dfrac{2}{3}}S_r$ so that $PD_r = \dfrac{S_r}{\sqrt{6}} = 0.408S_r$. From the relationship between MD_r and S_r and the values in *Table 11* it can be seen that $PE_r = 0.839 MD_r = 0.685 S_r$, $PC_{r25} = 0.481 MD_r = 0.392 S_r$, $PC_{75} = 1.346 MD_r = 1.099 S_r$, etc. The values of other measures of dispersion for the Normal Probability Surface, the Circular Uniform Surface, and the Mean Deviation Surface will be mentioned in the section dealing with relative dispersion in the next chapter.

5Stewart and Warntz [96], pp. 99-108; Clark [17]; Stewart [94].

TABLE 10

DENSITIES OF THE MEAN DEVIATION SURFACE

At distances $\frac{r}{MD_\gamma}$ from the Median
Center, Expressed as Decimal
Fractions of the Maximum
Central Density D_c.

$\frac{r}{MD_\gamma}$	$\frac{D_x}{D_c}$	$\frac{r}{MD_\gamma}$	$\frac{D_x}{D_c}$	$\frac{r}{MD_\gamma}$	$\frac{D_x}{D_c}$
0.00	1.0000	1.45	.0550	2.90	.0030
0.05	.9048	1.50	.0498	2.95	.0027
0.10	.8187	1.55	.0450	3.00	.0025
0.15	.7408	1.60	.0408	3.05	.0022
0.20	.6703	1.65	.0369	3.10	.0020
0.25	.6065	1.70	.0334	3.15	.0018
0.30	.5488	1.75	.0302	3.20	.0017
0.35	.4966	1.80	.0273	3.25	.0015
0.40	.4493	1.85	.0247	3.30	.0014
0.45	.4066	1.90	.0224	3.35	.0012
0.50	.3679	1.95	.0202	3.40	.0011
0.55	.3329	2.00	.0183	3.45	.0010
0.60	.3012	2.05	.0166	3.50	.0009
0.65	.2725	2.10	.0150		
0.70	.2466	2.15	.0136	3.60	.0007
0.75	.2231	2.20	.0123	3.70	.0006
0.80	.2019	2.25	.0111	3.80	.0005
0.85	.1827	2.30	.0100	3.90	.0004
0.90	.1653	2.35	.0091	4.00	.0003
0.95	.1496	2.40	.0082	4.10	.0003
1.00	.1353	2.45	.0074	4.20	.0002
1.05	.1225	2.50	.0067	4.30	.0002
1.10	.1108	2.55	.0061	4.40	.0002
1.15	.1003	2.60	.0055	4.50	.0001
1.20	.0907	2.65	.0050	4.60	.0001
1.25	.0821	2.70	.0045	4.70	.0001
1.30	.0743	2.75	.0041	4.80	.0001
1.35	.0672	2.80	.0037	4.90	.0001
1.40	.0608	2.85	.0034	5.00	.0000*

*This value approaches but never actually reaches zero. It is shown here as such only because the values in this table are rounded to four decimal places.

TABLE 11

VOLUMES UNDER THE MEAN DEVIATION SURFACE

Population Included Within a Circle

Having Radius $\frac{r}{MD_r}$ with the Median

Center as Origin, Expressed as
a Decimal Fraction of the
Total Propulation.

$\frac{r}{MD_r}$	$\frac{P_x}{P}$	$\frac{r}{MD_r}$	$\frac{P_x}{P}$	$\frac{r}{MD_r}$	$\frac{P_x}{P}$
0.00	.0000	1.45	.7854	2.90	.9794
0.05	.0047	1.50	.8008	2.95	.9811
0.10	.0175	1.55	.8153	3.00	.9826
0.15	.0370	1.60	.8288	3.05	.9841
0.20	.0616	1.65	.8414	3.10	.9854
0.25	.0902	1.70	.8531	3.15	.9866
0.30	.1219	1.75	.8641	3.20	.9877
0.35	.1558	1.60	.8743	3.25	.9887
0.40	.1912	1.85	.8838	3.30	.9897
0.45	.2275	1.90	.8926	3.35	.9905
0.50	.2642	1.95	.9008	3.40	.9913
0.55	.3010	2.00	.9084	3.45	.9920
0.60	.3374	2.05	.9154	3.50	.9927
0.65	.3732	2.10	.9220		
0.70	.4082	2.15	.9281	3.60	.9939
0.75	.4422	2.20	.9337	3.70	.9949
0.80	.4751	2.25	.9389	3.80	.9957
0.85	.5067	2.30	.9437	3.90	.9964
0.90	.5372	2.35	.9481	4.00	.9970
0.95	.5662	2.40	.9522	4.10	.9975
1.00	.5940	2.45	.9560	4.20	.9979
1.05	.6204	2.50	.9596	4.30	.9982
1.10	.6454	2.55	.9628	4.40	.9985
1.15	.6691	2.60	.9658	4.50	.9988
1.20	.6915	2.65	.9685	4.60	.9990
1.25	.7127	2.70	.9711	4.70	.9992
1.30	.7326	2.75	.9734	4.80	.9993
1.35	.7513	2.80	.9756	4.90	.9994
1.40	.7689	2.85	.9776	5.00	.9995

A graphic comparison of the density patterns for these three model surfaces is shown as *Figure 32*. Since the density function for the Mean Deviation Surface is an inverse first power exponential function, its density curve is linear on a semi-logarithmic grid such as *Figure 32*.

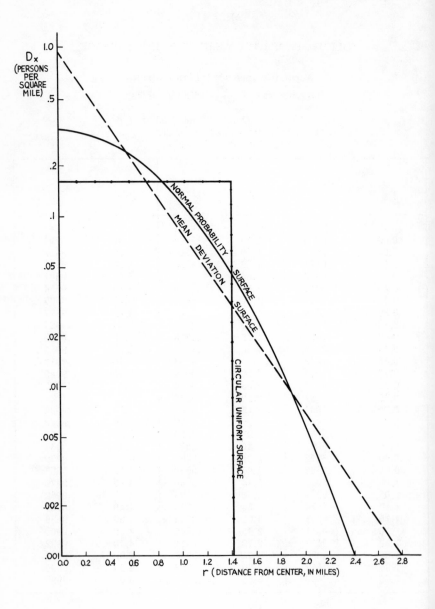

FIGURE 32.—Densities of Model Surfaces when $P=1$ person and $S_\gamma=1$ mile

One expected feature of this graph is that the Mean Deviation Surface, which was developed for the analysis of urban areas, has the largest central density. In fact, since its $D_c = \frac{2P}{\pi (MD_\gamma)^2}$ and, for the Normal Probability Surface $D_c = \frac{P}{\pi S_\gamma^2}$, and $S_\gamma \cong MD_\gamma$, the central density of a Mean Deviation Surface must be at least twice as great as the central density of a Normal Probability Surface where P and S_γ are the same for both distributions.

Some Applications of the Normal Probability Surface,
the Circular Uniform Surface and the Mean
Deviation Surface

The proportion of the populations $\left(\frac{P_x}{P}\right)$ within $\frac{1}{2}S_\gamma$, S_γ, $2S_\gamma$, $3S_\gamma$, and $4S_\gamma$, of S_c for the seven nations and the three models are shown in *Table 12*. The values in the table speak for themselves and further discussion of them here is not necessary. Corresponding values or the history of the United States population are presented in *Table 13*. The most interesting feature of these results is the concentration of this population for the last century. During this period the proportion of the population within $\frac{1}{2}S_\gamma$ and S_γ in the United States has been greater than the corresponding proportion for the Normal Probability Surface. In addition, the proportion within $2S_\gamma$ in the United States has been less than the value for the Normal Probability Surface since 1860.

Additional applications of these model surfaces will be discussed in Chapters VII and IX.

TABLE 12

THE PROPORTIONS OF THE POPULATIONS OF SEVEN NATIONS WITHIN CERTAIN DISTANCES OR THE ARITHMETIC MEAN CENTER

Nations	Distances from S_c.				
	$\frac{1}{2}S_\gamma$	S_γ	$2S_\gamma$	$3S_\gamma$	$4S_\gamma$
Australia	.277	.822	.933	.998	1.000
United Kingdom	.292	.708	.981	.998	1.000*
Brazil	.203	.614	.985	1.000*	1.000
Japan	.296	.693	.953	1.000	
United States	.287	.743	.930	1.000	
India	.084	.632	.995	1.000	
China	.207	.726	.969	.997	1.000
Normal Probability Surface	.2212	.6321	.9817	.9999	1.0000*
Circular Uniform Surface	.1250	.5000	1.0000		
Mean Deviation Surface	.3463	.7022	.9560	.9946	.9994

*This value is less than one. It is shown here as one only because the values are rounded to three and four decimal places.

TABLE 13

THE PROPORTIONS OF THE POPULATION OF THE UNITED STATES WITHIN CERTAIN DISTANCES OF THE ARITHMETIC MEAN CENTER, 1754-1960

Date	Distances from S_c:				
	$\frac{1}{2S_\gamma}$	S_γ	$2S_\gamma$	$3S_\gamma$	$4S_\gamma$
1754	.288	.626	.949	1.0000	
1775	.283	.625	.969	1.0000	
1790	.302	.613	.986	1.0000	
1800	.283	.592	.994	.9983	1.0000
1810	.280	.601	.981	.9986	1.0000
1820	.226	.624	.971	1.0000	
1830	.229	.620	.971	1.0000	
1840	.187	.613	.975	1.0000	
1850	.213	.665	.986	.9932	.9954
1860	.224	.729	.977	.9853	.9945
1870	.234	.740	.975	.9810	1.0000
1880	.251	.716	.968	.9772	1.0000
1890	.250	.739	.960	.9756	1.0000
1900	.265	.713	.957	.9801	1.0000
1910	.267	.761	.946	1.0000	
1920	.273	.766	.940	1.0000	
1930	.287	.777	.929	1.0000	
1940	.291	.775	.923	1.0000	
1950	.301	.769	.905	1.0000	
1960	.287	.743	.930	1.0000	
Normal Probability Surface	.2212	.6321	.9817	.9999	1.0000*
Circular Uniform Surface	.1250	.5000	1.0000		
Mean Deviation Surface	.3463	.7022	.9560	.9946	.9994

*This value is less than one. It is shown here as one only because the value is rounded to four decimal places.

CHAPTER VII

RELATIVE DISPERSION, SPACING MEASURES, SKEWNESS, AND KURTOSIS

Measures of Relative Dispersion

The values of measures of dispersion for areal distributions are greatly influenced by the size of the area that is being studied. This makes it difficult to obtain meaningful comparisons of these parameters for different areas. To overcome this handicap we seek measures of relative dispersion whose values are independent of differences in area among the regions being analyzed.

All the measures of relative dispersion which will be introduced here have two features in common. First, they indicate the dispersion of a distribution *relative* to its area. In addition, their values are always pure numbers, independent of units. This is caused by the fact that all measures of relative dispersion are defined as the ratio of two distances.

There are two basic ways to define such parameters. One obvious method would be simply to divide the value of one of the distance deviations by the value of a function of the size of the area, where the latter is in units of distance. Thus $\frac{MD_r}{r_A}$, $\frac{S_r}{r_A}$, and $\frac{H_r}{r_A}$ would be measures of relative dispersion. The values of these parameters have a limited range. The minimum value is obviously zero. Maximum dispersion occurs when the two items that determine the distance range comprise the total population. In this case $MD_r = S_r = H_r = \frac{W}{2}$. Therefore, the maximum possible value for these measures is $\frac{W}{2r_A}$. Of course, this limit is itself a variable which depends on the shape of the area. In fact $1 \leqq \frac{W}{2r_A} < \infty$. However, for almost all areal distributions $1 \leqq \frac{W}{2r_A} \leqq 4$.

The values of $\frac{W}{2r_A}, \frac{MD_r}{r_A}, \frac{S_r}{r_A}$, and $\frac{H_r}{r_A}$ for the distributions of population in the seven nations are shown in *Table 14*. Corresponding results for the history of the distribution of population in the United States are presented in *Table 15*.

These three parameters, $\frac{MD_r}{r_A}$, $\frac{S_r}{r_A}$, and $\frac{H_r}{r_A}$ have three disadvantages as measures of relative dispersion:

1. Their values, while independent of the size of the area, are influenced by the shape of the area. This is true because the limiting value, $\frac{W}{2r_A}$, is

TABLE 14

MEASURES OF RELATIVE DISPERSION BASED ON r_A FOR THE
DISTRIBUTIONS OF POPULATION IN SEVEN NATIONS

Nation	$\frac{W}{2r_A}$	$\frac{MD_r}{r_A}$	$\frac{S_r}{r_A}$	$\frac{H_r}{r_A}$
Australia	1.27	0.45	0.63	0.08
United Kingdom	2.17	0.66	0.77	0.15
Brazil	1.25	0.58	0.68	0.12
Japan	3.33	1.00	1.20	0.31
United States	1.49	0.69	0.86	0.15
India	1.42	0.76	0.85	0.46
China	1.38	0.44	0.52	0.23

TABLE 15

MEASURES OF RELATIVE DISPERSION BASED ON r_A FOR THE
DISTRIBUTION OF POPULATION IN THE
UNITED STATES, 1754-1960

Date	$\frac{W}{2r_A}$	$\frac{MD_r}{r_A}$	$\frac{S_r}{r_A}$	$\frac{H_r}{r_A}$
1754	2.30	0.75	0.88	0.31
1775	1.22	0.43	0.50	0.20
1790	1.24	0.43	0.53	0.22
1800	1.59	0.45	0.58	0.23
1810	1.21	0.36	0.46	0.18
1820	1.20	0.40	0.49	0.19
1830	1.21	0.44	0.51	0.20

TABLE 15--Continued

Date	$\dfrac{W}{2r_A}$	$\dfrac{MD_r}{r_A}$	$\dfrac{S_r}{r_A}$	$\dfrac{H_r}{r_A}$
1840	1.21	0.48	0.54	0.21
1850	1.50	0.40	0.48	0.16
1860	1.49	0.45	0.54	0.16
1870	1.49	0.46	0.57	0.16
1880	1.49	0.49	0.60	0.17
1890	1.49	0.52	0.64	0.17
1900	1.49	0.54	0.66	0.16
1910	1.49	0.57	0.70	0.15
1920	1.49	0.59	0.72	0.15
1930	1.49	0.60	0.76	0.14
1940	1.49	0.61	0.78	0.14
1950	1.49	0.65	0.82	0.15
1960	1.49	0.69	0.86	0.15

determined by the shape of the area. When the area is a circle $W=2r_A$ and $\dfrac{W}{2r_A} = 1$. Therefore, the value of $\dfrac{S_r}{r_A}$ in Japan can be 1.20 only because of the shape of the area of that country. The ratio of W to $2r_A$ varies directly as the ratio of the length of the area to its width.

2. The most important theoretical model of an areal distribution is the Normal Probability Surface. Since $r_A = \infty$ for this model, meaningful standard values of these three measures of relative position for the Normal Probability Surface cannot be computed.

3. As indicated earlier, total area itself often has little meaning since it changes suddenly, often due to purely political factors.

The last of these weaknesses can be easily overcome by substituting r_a for r_A. Values of measures of relative dispersion based on r_a for the seven nations are shown in *Table 16*. These results indicate that the Australian population exhibits the greatest dispersion in relation to the effectively settled area around MD_C and S_C while the populations of China and the United Kingdom have the least relative dispersion around these two average positions. The greatest dispersion around H_C is found in India which supports previous conclusions about the "weakness" of the peak of potential in that country. The populations of the United States, the United Kingdom, Brazil, and Australia all exhibit great concentration about H_C.

TABLE 16

MEASURES OF RELATIVE DISPERSION BASED ON r_a FOR THE
DISTRIBUTIONS OF POPULATION IN SEVEN NATIONS

Nation	$\dfrac{W}{2r_a}$	$\dfrac{MD_r}{r_a}$	$\dfrac{S_r}{r_a}$	$\dfrac{H_r}{r_a}$
Australia	3.29	1.17	1.63	0.20
United Kingdom	2.17	0.66	0.77	0.15
Brazil	1.95	0.91	1.06	0.19
Japan	3.33	1.00	1.20	0.31
United States	1.62	0.75	0.94	0.15
India	1.49	0.80	0.89	0.48
China	1.98	0.64	0.75	0.33

Values of the measures of relative dispersion, based on r_a for the distribution of population over time in the United States, are presented in *Table 17* and plotted in *Figure 33*. This graph has several interesting features. The most obvious is that the upper limit, $\dfrac{W}{2r_a}$, is subject to violent fluctuations. This is caused by the instability of W, which is determined by the location of only two items of the entire population. In spite of this, the values of $\dfrac{S_r}{r_a}$, $\dfrac{MD_r}{r_a}$, and $\dfrac{H_r}{r_a}$ have been remarkably stable. Both $\dfrac{S_r}{r_a}$ and $\dfrac{MD_r}{r_a}$ displayed a similar pattern: a decreasing trend until 1840, approximately constant values between 1840 and 1940, and a rising tendency since 1940. The increasing dominance of the New York City peak of potential and the increasing concentration around H_c is shown by the declining values of $\dfrac{H_r}{r_a}$. However, measures of relative dispersion are best suited for comparisons among different areas. For analysis of changing patterns during a period of time in a region, ordinary absolute measures of dispersion yield more meaningful results. In the case of the demographic history of the United States, the measures of relative dispersion conceal the effect of westward expansion since the values of r_a were increasing just as rapidly as the values of S_γ and MD_γ.

TABLE 17

MEASURES OF RELATIVE DISPERSION BASED ON r_a FOR
THE DISTRIBUTION OF POPULATION IN THE
UNITED STATES, 1754-1960

Date	$\dfrac{W}{2r_a}$	$\dfrac{MD_\gamma}{r_a}$	$\dfrac{S_\gamma}{r_a}$	$\dfrac{\bar{H}_\gamma}{r_a}$
1754	3.09	1.00	1.18	0.41
1775	2.64	0.93	1.08	0.43
1790	2.36	0.82	1.02	0.42
1800	2.68	0.76	0.97	0.38
1810	2.46	0.74	0.94	0.36
1820	2.24	0.75	0.91	0.35
1830	2.02	0.73	0.86	0.33
1840	1.79	0.70	0.79	0.31
1850	2.60	0.70	0.83	0.28
1860	2.35	0.70	0.85	0.25
1870	2.28	0.70	0.86	0.24
1880	2.05	0.68	0.83	0.23
1890	1.84	0.65	0.79	0.21
1900	1.85	0.67	0.82	0.20
1910	1.71	0.66	0.81	0.17
1920	1.67	0.66	0.81	0.17
1930	1.66	0.67	0.84	0.16
1940	1.62	0.67	0.85	0.16
1950	1.62	0.71	0.90	0.16
1960	1.62	0.75	0.94	0.15

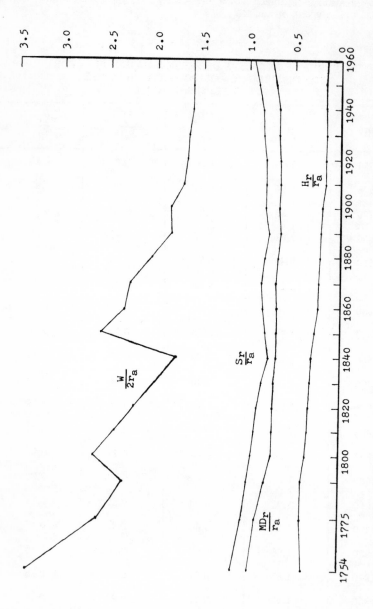

FIGURE 33.—Measures of Relative Dispersion Based on r_a for the Distribution of Population in the United States, 1754-1960

The use of r_a as a denominator solves only one of three difficulties associated with the measures of relative dispersion that have been defined in this section. In order to overcome the remaining two weaknesses, a different type of measure must be introduced. Any ratio of two measures of dispersion based on moments, where the measure based on the higher order moment is the denominator, will indicate relative dispersion. This definition had been used in linear statistics where the ratio of the mean deviation to the standard deviation is often employed as a measure of relative dispersion. Three measures of this type will be used in this study: $\frac{MD_\gamma}{S_\gamma}$, $\frac{H_\gamma}{S_\gamma}$, and $\frac{H_\gamma}{MD_\gamma}$.

Values of these parameters for certain theoretical areal distributions can be obtained without difficulty. For the Normal Probability Surface, the areal moments about S_c are governed by the following relationship: $M_{2\alpha} = M_2^{\alpha} [\Gamma(1+\alpha)] = S_\gamma^{2\alpha} [\Gamma(1+\alpha)]$ where $\alpha > -1$. When $\alpha = \frac{1}{2}$, $M_1 = \frac{\sqrt{\pi}}{2} S_\gamma$. When $\alpha = -\frac{1}{2}$, $M_{-1} = \frac{\sqrt{\pi}}{S_\gamma}$. For the Normal Probability Surface all average positions coincide so that $M_1 = MD_\gamma$ and $M_{-1} = \frac{1}{H_\gamma}$. Thus, $\frac{MD_\gamma}{S_\gamma} = \frac{\sqrt{\pi}}{2} = 0.886$ and $\frac{H_\gamma}{S_\gamma} = \frac{1}{\sqrt{\pi}} = 0.564$. Therefore, $\frac{H_\gamma}{MD_\gamma} = \frac{2}{\pi} = 0.637$.

In the case of the Circular Uniform Surface, the measures of dispersion are functionally related to the radius of the circle: $H_\gamma = \frac{\gamma}{2}$, $MD_\gamma = \frac{2\gamma}{3}$, and $S_\gamma = \frac{\gamma}{\sqrt{2}}$. Thus, $\frac{MD_\gamma}{S_\gamma} = \frac{2\sqrt{2}}{3} = 0.943$; $\frac{H_\gamma}{S_\gamma} = \frac{1}{\sqrt{2}} = 0.707$, and $\frac{H_\gamma}{MD_\gamma} = \frac{3}{4} = 0.750$.

For the Mean Deviation Surface, $\frac{MD_\gamma}{S_\gamma} = \sqrt{\frac{2}{3}} = 0.816$, $\frac{H_\gamma}{MD_\gamma} = \frac{1}{2}$, so $\frac{H_\gamma}{S_\gamma} = \frac{1}{\sqrt{6}} = 0.408$.

The values of these parameters for the actual distributions of population in the seven nations are included in *Table 18*. The most general feature of these results is the indication of the concentration of these distributions, particularly when H_γ is the numerator of the ratio. None of the seven populations have a value of $\frac{H_\gamma}{S_\gamma}$ or $\frac{H_\gamma}{MD_\gamma}$ that is as large as the value for the Normal Probability Surface. Only for India and China do the actual values exceed the standard for the Mean Deviation Surface model. The relative dispersion, as indicated by $\frac{H_\gamma}{S_\gamma}$ and $\frac{H_\gamma}{MD_\gamma}$, is very small for the other five populations. When $\frac{MD_\gamma}{S_\gamma}$ is used, only Australia and the United States exhibit greater concentration than all three models. The population of India is the only one of the seven which is more dispersed than both exponential models.

Values of these three measures for the distribution of population over time in the United States are presented in *Table 19*. Once again the concentration of these distributions is apparent. From *Figure 34* it can be seen that all the

TABLE 18

MEASURES OF RELATIVE DISPERSION BASED ON RATIOS OF MEASURES OF DISPERSION FOR THE DISTRIBUTIONS OF POPULATION IN SEVEN NATIONS

Nation	$\dfrac{MD_\gamma}{S_\gamma}$	$\dfrac{H_\gamma}{S_\gamma}$	$\dfrac{H_\gamma}{MD_\gamma}$
Australia	0.715	0.122	0.170
United Kingdom	0.858	0.194	0.226
Brazil	0.852	0.176	0.207
Japan	0.832	0.258	0.310
United States	0.795	0.174	0.219
India	0.892	0.541	0.606
China	0.855	0.437	0.511
Normal Probability Surface	0.886	0.564	0.637
Circular Uniform Surface	0.943	0.707	0.750
Mean Deviation Surface	0.816	0.408	0.500

values of $\dfrac{MD_\gamma}{S_\gamma}$ and $\dfrac{H_\gamma}{S_\gamma}$ have been less than the corresponding values for the Normal Probability Surface. This is also true for $\dfrac{H_\gamma}{MD_\gamma}$, although this is not shown on the graph. There has also been a definite trend since 1840 toward increasing concentration. By 1910 all three measures indicated greater concentration than the Mean Deviation Surface model.

Spacing Measures

Some of the most commonly employed techniques of areal analysis involve measures based on the distance between particular pairs of items of the population. One of the first of these methods was proposed by Barnes and Robinson [6] in 1940. They assumed that a population of farmhouses in a given area was evenly distributed in a hexagonal pattern. The area occupied by each farm is equal to $\dfrac{A}{P}$ and has the shape of a hexagon. If the diameter of this hexagon is $2r_H$, then $\dfrac{A}{P} = \dfrac{1}{2}\sqrt{3(2r_H)^2}$ and $2r_H = \sqrt{\dfrac{2A}{P\sqrt{3}}} = 1.07\sqrt{\dfrac{A}{P}}$. The constant was originally

TABLE 19

MEASURES OF RELATIVE DISPERSION BASED ON RATIOS OF MEASURES OF DISPERSION FOR THE DISTRIBUTION OF POPULATION IN THE UNITED STATES, 1754-1960

Date	$\dfrac{MD_\gamma}{S_\gamma}$	$\dfrac{H_\gamma}{S_\gamma}$	$\dfrac{H_\gamma}{MD_\gamma}$
1754	0.854	0.350	0.410
1775	0.855	0.397	0.464
1790	0.808	0.413	0.511
1800	0.785	0.393	0.500
1810	0.782	0.383	0.491
1820	0.825	0.384	0.465
1830	0.849	0.388	0.457
1840	0.883	0.385	0.435
1850	0.842	0.340	0.404
1860	0.822	0.292	0.356
1870	0.815	0.282	0.346
1880	0.821	0.279	0.340
1890	0.819	0.265	0.324
1900	0.826	0.247	0.299
1910	0.815	0.216	0.265
1920	0.814	0.206	0.253
1930	0.793	0.188	0.236
1940	0.785	0.183	0.233
1950	0.786	0.177	0.225
1960	0.795	0.174	0.219
Normal Probability Surface	0.886	0.564	0.637
Circular Uniform Surface	0.943	0.707	0.750
Mean Deviation Surface	0.816	0.408	0.500

112

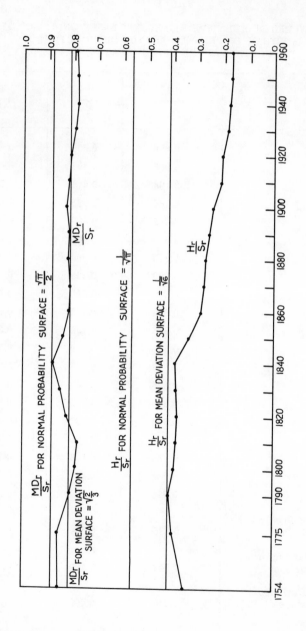

FIGURE 34. — $\frac{MD_r}{S_r}$ and $\frac{H_r}{S_r}$ for the Distribution of Population in the United States, 1754-1960

stated as *1.11* by Barnes and Robinson but the correct value of *1.07* appeared in an article by Mather [65] in 1944. There are two serious limitations associated with this technique: the values depend on the size of the areal units and a uniform distribution of the population is assumed. An advantage of this method is that it can be used for grouped, as well as ungrouped, data since knowledge of the exact locations of the items of the population in any class is not necessary. Thus, for populations that are approximately uniformly distributed, $2r_H$ can be a useful measure of dispersion, particularly when values of $2r_H$ for several areas can be compared.

Shortly after these articles were published, plant ecologists began to use distances between items as a measure of dispersion for areal distributions. Viktorov [108] started measuring straight line distances between plants. Cottam and Curtis [20] introduced sampling techniques and used the mean distance between pairs of randomly selected trees as a measure of dispersion. A review of all of these early efforts in ecology was written by Goodall [40] in 1952.

The basic measure of dispersion for areal distributions that was adopted by plant ecologists was the arithmetic mean of the actual distances between each item of the population and its Nth nearest neighbor $(\bar{r}_N)$. When $N=1$ this parameter is usually called the *mean distance to nearest neighbor*. If r_N is the distance between a given item and its N order neighbor, $\bar{r}_N = \dfrac{\sum_{N=1}^{P} \left(r_N \right)}{P}$. The next advance in the theory of nearest neighbor analysis was supplied by Dice [26], who designed a test to measure the difference between the actual distribution and a random distribution. However, this test involved a complicated statistic based on the third moment and it was soon discarded.

Dice's method was supplanted by procedures devised by Clark and Evans [18]. They defined an infinitely large random distribution over an infinitely large area as having a given density, D_A. Then, when $N=1$, an expected value of the mean distance to nearest neighbor $(\bar{\rho}_N)$ can be calculated for this model. In fact, $\bar{\rho}_N = \dfrac{1}{2\sqrt{D_A}}$. The basic measure used by Clark and Evans, R_N, is the ratio of the observed to the expected value $\left(R_N = \dfrac{\bar{r}_N}{\bar{\rho}_N} \right)$. When the entire population is concentrated at one position, $r_N = 0$, and thus, $\bar{r}_N = 0$. If the actual population is randomly distributed $\bar{r}_N = \bar{\rho}_N$ and $R_N = 1$. The maximum value of R_N occurs when the population is distributed in a hexagonal pattern such that each item (except the peripheral ones) has 6 equidistant nearest neighbors. In this case, $R_N = 2.1491$.

In the past decade there have been many contributions to the techniques of using nearest neighbor analysis to measure the degree of randomness in an areal distribution. Skellam [83] introduced the assumption of a Poisson distribution for the probability of occurrence of z points within distance r of an aribitrary point x. Using this assumption, Morisita [69] and Thompson [102] independently derived the expected distance to the Nth nearest neighbor in a random distribution. They derived the probability density function for r_N,

$$f(r_N) = \frac{2\pi^N}{\Gamma(N)} r^{(2N-1)} e^{-\pi r^2}$$

For $N=1$ (nearest neighbor), this becomes $f(r_N) = 2\pi r e^{-\pi r^2}$. Dacey [23, 25] has derived the expression for the moment functions of r_N about the origin; $M_n = \dfrac{\Gamma(N+\frac{n}{2})}{\Gamma(N) \cdot \left(\pi^{\frac{n}{2}}\right)}$.

From these formulations, several techniques for testing the degree of randomness of an areal distribution have been developed.[1] These tests have been applied extensively to plant and animal populations. Recently, Dacey [23] has used these methods to investigate the distribution of towns having certain common characteristics. In general, nearest neighbor methods have proven satisfactory for detecting random tendencies of certain areal distributions. However, these procedures have one important drawback. The values of the dispersion parameters ($\bar{r}_N$, for example) depend on the knowledge of the precise location of every item in the population. Thus, this type of analysis cannot be used when only grouped data are available.

The original purpose of this type of analysis was to provide a quantitative indication of the spacing or spread of an areal distribution. The *arithmetic mean distance between N^{th} nearest neighbors*, $\bar{r}_N$, is a measure of areal dispersion. While nearest neighbor analysis is useful for indicating randomness, r_N and similar measures have little value as indicators of areal dispersion. The disadvantage of not being able to use grouped data has already been mentioned. Even when ungrouped data are available, the necessary amount of computation and measurement of distances is likely to be prohibitive unless P is very small.

Another defect arises from the fact that every item of the population is not considered in conjunction with every other item. Therefore, the basic features of the dispersion of an areal distribution can be obscured by the relationships between nearest neighbors. This is especially true when the items of the population display a tendency to cluster in small groups. As an example, if values of $\bar{r}_N$ were calculated for the human population of the United States, these values would show almost no change for the entire history of the country. This would be true even for moderately large values of N, and, as N increases, the necessary amount of computation and measurement increases very rapidly. Therefore, if $\bar{r}_N$ was used as a measure of dispersion for the United States population, the macroscopic westward expansion of the population would be completely lost in the microscopic analysis of distance to nearest neighbors.

Fortunately, these disadvantages can be easily overcome by using MD_P as a measure of dispersion. As stated previously, the latter is the mean distance between *all possible pairs* of the population and it can be computed, without much difficulty, from grouped data.

Skewness

In linear statistics, measures of skewness relate to the degree of asymmetry of the frequency curve. A symmetrical curve exists when the positions of the mean, the median, and the mode coincide. In such a case, the shape of the curve is the same in both directions as the distance from this center increases.

---

[1]See Dacey [24].

When these concepts are extended to areal distributions, the definition of symmetry is not so obvious. Indeed, two different kinds, *radial symmetry* and *areal symmetry*, can be defined. A necessary condition for both of these is that S_C, MD_C, and H_C coincide. For any areal distribution, an infinite number of planes can be constructed passing through this central position and perpendicular to the surface of the area. The intersection of the frequency surface with such a plane will appear as a curve on the plane. For a distribution to have radial symmetry, all of these curves (one for each of the infinite number of planes) must be exactly the same and they must have linear symmetry. For a distribution to have areal symmetry all of these curves must simply have linear symmetry. Thus, if a distribution has radial symmetry, it must also have areal symmetry.

Three examples of this are the Circular Uniform Surface, the Normal Probability Surface and the Mean Deviation Surface. However, if a population is uniformly distributed over a rectangular area, the resulting frequency surface has only areal symmetry. The measures to be discussed in this section are based solely on the concept of areal symmetry—an areal distribution having this property will be considered symmetrical.

The most common measure of skewness for linear statistics was defined by Karl Pearson as the value, arithmetic mean minus the mode, divided by the standard deviation. Since both the numerator and denominator of this expression are measured in the same units, the resulting quotient is a pure number, independent of units. For a symmetrical distribution its value is obviously zero. In the case of an asymmetrical curve, the sign of this measure depends upon whether the arithmetic mean lies to the left or to the right of the mode.

Pearson's measure of skewness has been shown to be applicable to areal distributions.[2] If r_{SO} is the distance between S_c and MO_c then the skewness, SK_P, equals $\dfrac{r_{SO}}{S_r}$. The subscript "P" is used because this parameter is based solely on the distribution of population—the shape of the area involved is not considered. Since both r_{SO} and S_r are distances, SK_P is a pure number. For a distribution having areal symmetry $r_{SO} = O$, and thus $SK_P = O$. Of course, the value of SK_P can never be negative since all distances must be equal to or greater than zero. However, one may indicate the compass direction of skewness, with its bearing being that of the line from MO_c to S_c. The one serious shortcoming of SK_P is that it depends on MO_c and all the weaknesses of that measure affect SK_P.

It is possible to consider the measurement of areal skewness in a totally different way. If a population is symmetrically distributed over an area, A, then S_C coincides with A_c. Thus, for a given distribution, the distance between S_C and A_c (represented by r_{AP}) provides an indication of skewness. This permits the introduction of a new measure of skewness SK_A, which is equal to $\dfrac{r_{AP}}{r_A}$. This measure is obviously influenced by the shape of the area: hence, the subscript "A". SK_A is also a ratio of distances, and thus, a pure number. When this

---

[2]Warntz and Neft [119], pp. 53, 65 and Warntz [115].

measure is used, the compass direction of skewness has the bearing of the line from S_c to A_c. For a distribution having areal symmetry $r_{AP}= 0$ and so $SK_A = 0$.

However, one disadvantage of this parameter is that SK_A may have a value of zero for a distribution that does not have areal symmetry. For example, $SK_A = O$ for any uniformly distributed population, regardless of the shape of the area. This is not too serious because such examples rarely occur. In addition, it can be argued that any uniform distribution does have a kind of "areal symmetry".

For any measure based on total area, there can be a corresponding measure based on the effectively settled area. Thus, one can define $SK_a = \dfrac{r_{aP}}{r_a}$ where r_{ap} is the distance between S_c and a_c. This measure has the same properties as SK_A.

In practice, the values of SK_P rarely are close to the values of SK_A and/or SK_a. This is understandable since these parameters are intended to measure different forms of skewness. A hypothetical illustration may serve to show this more clearly. The area, A, of this hypothetical distribution is shown in *Figure 35.* The population, P, is distributed according to the Normal Probability Surface model over the circular area centered on "Y" with radius "y", and the density of population at A_c is greater than two persons per square mile. The rest of A is uninhabited.

The question arises as to whether or not this distribution has areal symmetry. If only the distribution of the population is considered, and the shape of the total area is ignored, the distribution is surely symmetrical. S_c, MD_c, H_c, and MO_c all coincide at Y. Thus $r_{SO}=O$ and $SK_P=O$. However, when the uninhabited portion of A is considered, the distribution of P with respect to the total area, A, is clearly not symmetrical. In this case, the curves formed by the intersection of the frequency surface with the planes passing through Y and perpendicular to the surface of A are not all symmetrical. This also can be indicated by calculating SK_A as follows:

$$A = \pi y^2 + (2y)^2 = \pi y^2 + 4y^2 = (\pi + 4)y^2.$$

$$r_A = \left(\frac{A}{\pi}\right)^{\frac{1}{2}} = \left[\frac{(4+\pi)y^2}{\pi}\right]^{\frac{1}{2}} = 1.50773y.$$

$$r_{AP} = y.$$

$$SK_A = \frac{r_{AP}}{r_A} = \frac{y}{1.50773y} = 0.663.$$

Of course, if SK_a were used as the measure of skewness, the uninhabited region would be removed from consideration. Since a_c is at Y, $SK_a=O$. However, these results are not meant to create the impression that SK_P and SK_a must have similar values. All three measures of areal skewness are based on different

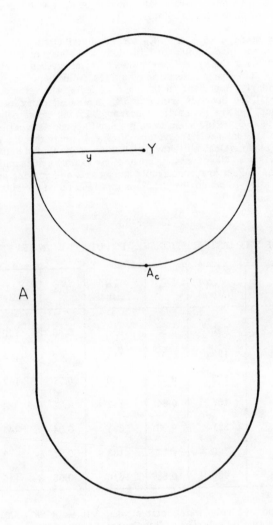

FIGURE 35.—Hypothetical Distribution to Illustrate the Differences
Among the Measures of Skewness

definitions and may have greatly different values for the same population. The investigator who uses these parameters must determine which one is the most appropriate for any particular problem.

The values of SK_P, SK_A, and SK_a for the distribution of population in the seven nations used as examples in this study are shown in *Table 20*. For the purpose of comparing the values of skewness among various countries, SK_A is the best of the three parameters. SK_P suffers from the weaknesses of MO_c. This is particularly important in the case of India, where the distribution is distinctly bimodal and possibly trimodal. SK_a is a satisfactory measure, but in analyzing nations, we are primarily concerned with the entire political area of the country. Thus, SK_A would seem to be the most appropriate parameter to use in this particular instance. The values of SK_A indicate that the population of India is nearly symmetrical while the populations of the United States and China are moderately skew. The other four populations exhibit a substantial degree of skewness. These values are comparable among areas of varying sizes because they all are ratios in which the denominator depends on the size of the area.

TABLE 20

SKEWNESS OF THE DISTRIBUTIONS OF POPULATION IN SEVEN NATIONS

Nation	r_{SO} (miles)	SK_P	r_{AP} (miles)	SK_A	r_{aP} (miles)	SK_a
Australia	340	0.55	860	0.88	100	0.27
United Kingdom	123	0.92	114	0.69	114	0.69
Brazil	505	0.72	730	0.71	187	0.29
Japan	165	0.64	141	0.71	141	0.71
United States	821	0.98	524	0.54	449	0.50
India	590	1.17	133	0.21	78	0.13
China	480	0.83	610	0.55	115	0.15

There is no set rule which states what values of SK_P, SK_A, or SK_a are necessary in order to refer to a distribution as "moderately skew" or "extremely skew". However, for a given distribution, SK_P will usually have a greater value than SK_A, and SK_A will almost always have a larger value than SK_a. It is interesting to note that, when only the effectively settled area is considered, four of these seven distributions (India, China, Australia, and Brazil) are nearly symmetrical.

The values of SK_P and SK_A for the distribution of population over time in the United States are shown in *Table 21* and *Figure 36*. In this case SK_A is not a very good measure because sudden changes in political boundaries cause sudden large changes in the location of A_c. SK_a would be a very useful parameter in this situation, but early data dealing with effectively settled area are difficult to obtain and evaluate so that values of SK_a were not computed. The values of SK_p also show great fluctuations due to early shifts in the location of MO_c. However, the modal center has been in New York City since 1820 and this position was firmly established as the only possible modal center by 1840. Therefore, since 1840, the values of SK_p do provide an excellent indication of the skewness of the United States population. The amazing feature of these values is their constancy. In the last 120 years, SK_p has varied only between 0.90 and 1.01. This means that increases in the value of S_r have been approximately equal to increases in r_{SO}, the distance between S_c and New York City.

SK_A is a satisfactory measure for periods during which no sudden boundary changes occurred, which has been true in the United States for the last century. The decreasing trend of SK_A during this period indicates the westward movement of the population—S_c has been moving closer to A_c. The data in *Table 21* provide quantitative evidence that the distribution of population in the United States has always been characterized by a definite lack of symmetry.

TABLE 21

SKEWNESS OF THE DISTRIBUTION OF POPULATION IN
THE UNITED STATES, 1754-1960

Date	r_{SO} (miles)	SK_P	r_{AP} (miles)	SK_A
1754	299	1.25	177	0.65
1775	64	0.24	388	0.74
1790	78	0.28	371	0.71
1800	114	0.38	327	0.62
1810	147	0.43	722	0.98
1820	275	0.75	649	0.87
1830	313	0.82	616	0.82
1840	361	0.90	559	0.75
1850	414	0.90	927	0.96
1860	487	0.92	857	0.88
1870	527	0.96	810	0.83
1880	585	1.00	755	0.78
1890	631	1.01	703	0.72
1900	645	1.01	689	0.71
1910	683	1.00	654	0.67
1920	694	0.98	641	0.66
1930	717	0.97	623	0.64
1940	729	0.97	611	0.63
1950	772	0.96	571	0.59
1960	821	0.98	524	0.54

120

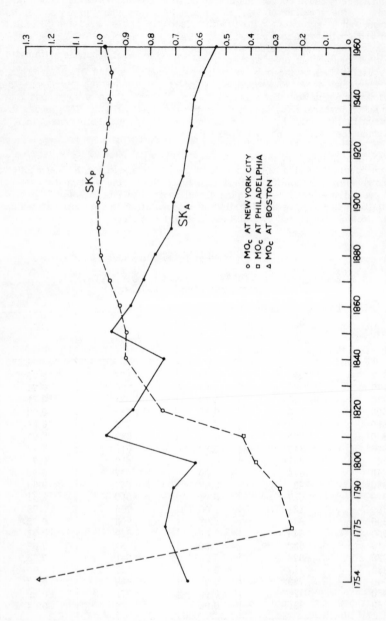

FIGURE 36.—SK_P and SK_A for the Distribution of Population in the United States, 1754–1960

Kurtosis

For any distribution, one of the most difficult characteristics to measure is its degree of kurtosis or peakedness. In linear statistics, the parameter that is most often used for this purpose is β_2, the ratio of the fourth moment about the arithmetic mean to the square of the second moment about the arithmetic mean. The value of β_2 for a normal distribution is 3. Thus, for a given linear distribution, if $\beta_2 > 3$ the distribution is said to be leptokurtic, if $\beta_2 < 3$ the distribution is platykurtic, and if $\beta_2 = 3$ the distribution is mesokurtic. This measure has several weaknesses[3] but it has proven to be more useful than any of the alternatives that have been suggested.

Even-numbered moments are used to indicate the kurtosis of linear distributions because negative values appear in the calculation of odd numbered moments. In the computation of areal moments all distances are positive so that any ratio of M_y to $M_z^{\frac{y}{z}}$, where $y > z > 0$, will indicate kurtosis. However, comparability with linear statistics is an important consideration so an areal β_2 can be defined as $\frac{M_4}{M_2^2}$. Since both the numerator and the denominator are in units of distance to the fourth power, β_2 for the case of a Normal Probability Surface distribution (the "normal" areal distribution) is obtainable from the expression relating the central areal moments of the model: $M_2^\propto = M_2^\propto \left[\Gamma(1 + \propto) \right]$. When $\propto = 2$, $M_4 = M_2^2 \left[\Gamma(3) \right] = 2M_2^2$. Thus, $\beta_2 = 2$ for the Normal Probability Surface. The possible range of the values of β_2 is from one to infinity.

The fact that β_2 has an infinite range and that the "normal" value is very close to one end of the range is one of the disadvantages of this measure because it means that a distribution of many values of β_2 is apt to be a very skew linear distribution. This becomes important when samples, rather than entire populations, are being analyzed. In this situation, it is helpful when the distribution of a sample statistic (sampling distribution) can be described as symmetrical or approximately normal. For this reason a new measure of kurtosis, K, will be defined as $\frac{\beta_2 - 2}{\beta_2}$. The range of this measure is: $-1 \leq K < +1$.

Therefore, a given areal distribution is leptokurtic if $K > 0$, platykurtic if $K < 0$, and mesokurtic if $K = 0$. Uniform distributions are obviously platykurtic. In the case of the Circular Uniform Surface $\beta_2 = \frac{4}{3}$ and $K = -\frac{1}{2}$. For the Normal Probability Surface, $K = 0$ since $\beta_2 = 2$, while, for the Mean Deviation Surface $\beta_2 = 3\frac{1}{3}$ and $K = +\frac{2}{5}$.

The values of β_2 and K for the distributions of human population in seven nations are shown in *Table 22*. The tendency of human populations to cluster means that most of these distributions will be leptokurtic. Among these examples, only Brazil and India have platykurtic populations. The low value of K in India

------

[3]See Mills [68], p. 173.

122

TABLE 22

KURTOSIS OF THE DISTRIBUTIONS OF POPULATION IN SEVEN NATIONS

Nation	β_2	K
Australia	4.61	+0.57
United Kingdom	2.35	+0.15
Brazil	1.77	−0.13
Japan	2.53	+0.21
United States	2.62	+0.24
India	1.54	−0.30
China	2.57	+0.22
Normal Probability Surface	2.00	0
Circular Uniform Surface	1.33	−0.50
Mean Deviation Surface	3.33	+0.40

is another addition to the increasing amount of quantitative evidence whic indicates that the Indian population is much more evenly distributed over i area than any of the other human populations mentioned in this study.

Values of β_2 and K for the distribution of population over time in the Unit States are presented in *Table 23* and the graph of K for this period is shown Figure 37. The most striking feature of these results is that the United State population has almost always been leptokurtic.

K actually measures the *relative* peakedness of a distribution—the concentra tion of the population in relation to the area over which it is distributed. There fore, sudden changes in area, without accompanying major shifts in populatio will produce a large increase in the value of K. The fluctuations of the gra in *Figure 37* clearly illustrate this principle. The two periods when there we sizable increases in K, between 1800 and 1810 and between 1840 and 186 were periods when large amounts of territory were acquired by the United State

After these changes in area, movement of people into this sparsely i habited territory caused the values of K to decline. Since 1940 this decline h been accelerated by the rapid increase of population along the Pacific Coas Of course, the value of K is truly meaningful only for a distinctly unimod distribution. If the west coast population continues to increase at its prese rate it may, one day, be advisable to divide the United States into two area Eastern and Western, in order to be able to compute meaningful paramete which indicate the kurtosis of this areal distribution of population.

TABLE 23

KURTOSIS OF THE DISTRIBUTION OF POPULATION
IN THE UNITED STATES, 1754-1960

Date	β_2	K
1754	2.39	+0.16
1775	2.14	+0.07
1790	2.01	+0.005
1800	1.99	-0.005
1810	2.41	+0.17
1820	2.32	+0.14
1830	2.06	+0.03
1840	1.99	-0.005
1850	4.03	+0.50
1860	4.84	+0.59
1870	4.78	+0.58
1880	4.28	+0.53
1890	3.92	+0.49
1900	3.70	+0.46
1910	3.46	+0.42
1920	3.34	+0.40
1930	3.39	+0.41
1940	3.31	+0.40
1950	2.94	+0.32
1960	2.62	+0.24
Normal Probability Surface	2.00	0
Circular Uniform Surface	1.33	-0.50
Mean Deviation Surface	3.33	+0.40

A summary of the values of various measures, indicating dispersion, relative dispersion, and kurtosis, for the three model surfaces discussed in chapter VI is shown as *Table 24*. These values can be used to see which model most closely approximates an actual areal distribution. The Circular Uniform surface is, of course, the most dispersed and platykurtic of the three, while the Mean Deviation Surface is the most concentrated and leptokurtic. Many of the values of these measures for the human populations which have been used as examples in this study are very close to the corresponding values of the Mean Deviation Surface. Some of the distributions resemble the Normal Probability surface model. None of these populations can be considered as being uniformly distributed.

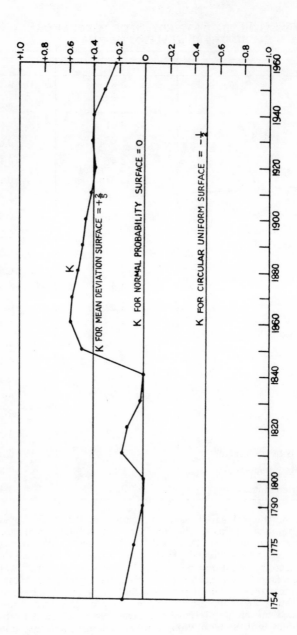

FIGURE 37.—Kurtosis of the Distribution of Population in the United States, 1754–1960

TABLE 24

DISPERSION, RELATIVE DISPERSION, AND KURTOSIS OF THREE MODEL SURFACES

	Normal Probability Surface	Circular Uniform Surface	Mean Deviation Surface
PE_γ	$\sqrt{\log_e 2}\, S_\gamma = 0.833 S_\gamma$	S_γ	$0.685 S_\gamma$
PD_γ	$\dfrac{S_\gamma}{\sqrt{2}} = 0.707 S_\gamma$	$\sqrt{2} S_\gamma = 1.414 S_\gamma$	$\dfrac{S_\gamma}{\sqrt{6}} = 0.408 S_\gamma$
$\dfrac{MD_\gamma}{S_\gamma}$	$\dfrac{\sqrt{\pi}}{2} = 0.886$	$\dfrac{4}{3\sqrt{2}} = 0.943$	$\sqrt{\dfrac{2}{3}} = 0.816$
$\dfrac{H_\gamma}{S_\gamma}$	$\dfrac{1}{\sqrt{\pi}} = 0.564$	$\dfrac{1}{\sqrt{2}} = 0.707$	$\dfrac{1}{\sqrt{6}} = 0.408$
$\dfrac{H_\gamma}{MD_\gamma}$	$\dfrac{2}{\pi} = 0.637$	$\dfrac{3}{4}$	$\dfrac{1}{2}$
β_2	2	$\dfrac{4}{3}$	$\dfrac{10}{3}$
K	0	$-\dfrac{1}{2}$	$+\dfrac{2}{5}$
$\dfrac{P_x}{P}$ Where x equals:			
$\dfrac{1}{2} S_\gamma$	0.2212	0.1250	0.3463
S_γ	0.6321	0.5000	0.7022
$2 S_\gamma$	0.9817	1.0000	0.9560
$3 S_\gamma$	0.9999		0.9946
$4 S_\gamma$	1.0000*		0.9994

*This value is less than one. It is shown here as one only because the value is rounded to four decimal places.

CHAPTER VIII
AREAL ASSOCIATION

Association Between Discrete Areal Variables

Geographers have long been interested in the degree of association among variables. Recently, there has been an increasing tendency to try to express such relationships quantitatively, using precise statistical measures of correlation rather than ambiguous verbal descriptions.

The first applications of correlation analysis to geographic data involved "site characteristics". These refer to the nature of a particular place so that values of the variable can be found from measurements at just that one place. Such values may not exert any influence on other locations. For example, Rose [78, 79] analyzed site characteristics when he examined the relationship between corn yields and temperature. Since site characteristics are independent of relative location, they can be treated as independent of areal distributions, and ordinary linear methods of correlation analysis can be used to determine the degree of association between such variables.

However, geographers are also concerned with relative locations or "position characteristics". This is particularly true in the field of industrial geography where the problem frequently arises of measuring the locational relationship between the markets for a certain product and the materials necessary to produce it. In this case, the problem is to measure the relationship between two areal distributions in order to determine the degree of areal association between them.

Unfortunately, most geographers have never actually measured areal association. They have merely transformed the macrogeographic position characteristics into microscopic discrete site characteristics and then used the well-established methods of analysis. Usually, the data are transformed into densities and a coefficient of correlation between the two density distributions is computed. This method suffers from two major defects. The first is that the coefficient of correlation is not influenced by the locational arrangement of the pairs of density values, so that relative location is not measured. Secondly, the coefficient of correlation thus computed is relative to the system of areal subdivision employed -the value of the coefficient tends to vary inversely with the number and directly with the area of the sub-divisions.

These difficulties have been noted by several individuals. In particular, Robinson and Bryson [77] have stated quite accurately that such a coefficient of correlation is subject to the possible error inherent in the derivation of any density value. Since density values are, in the limit, arbitrary, the magnitude of this error can be quite large. Many of the geographers who recognized this problem became convinced that it had no solution.

Association Between Areally Continuous Variables

Fortunately, Warntz [114, 116] has shown that a coefficient of correlation for areal distributions (coefficient of areal association) which is independent of an arbitrary areal framework can be easily obtained. This is achieved by using areally continuous macrogeographic variables derived from the microgeographic precise locations of discrete items. Ordinary methods of correlation analysis are then used to determine the degree of association between the two continuous surfaces.

When using areal data, the results of correlation analysis must be interpreted with caution because the observations are not strictly independent. This problem has been discussed by Neprash [71] and it is similar to the problem of correlating time series observations, a subject which is treated in most statistics texts.

However, before the methods of correlation analysis can be applied to a particular problem, the question arises as to how an areally continuous variable can be derived from a given density distribution. Actually, there is an infinite range of possible specific choices which fall under two major methods. The first method is to use a variable which has a specified functional relationship to the density distribution. For example, all areal moments are smooth continuous surfaces whose values can be calculated from a given density distribution. In this case, the problem becomes one of selecting the most appropriate surface to use in any particular situation. Usually, this will be the inverse first areal moment (or potential of population) because, for any position, potential measures the intensity of its accessibility to the distribution in the aggregate. Another factor is the close relationship that invariably exists between the potential surface and the density distribution.

A variable also can be selected by fitting a smoothed surface to the density distribution. The detailed procedures for selecting the most appropriate surface of closest possible fit are beyond the scope of this study. The best studies of this problem have been conducted by a geologist, W. C. Krumbein [58, 59, 60, 61]. Krumbein and Warntz have pioneered in the use of continuous areal variables for measuring areal association.

Once the appropriate macrogeographic variables have been selected, the only remaining problem is how to determine the degree of association between the two surfaces. Ideally, this would be accomplished by listing concommitant values of both variables for all of the infinite number of points in the area and then computing a coefficient of correlation from the listed data. Such a parameter could be described as the *population coefficient of areal association.*

Of course, this procedure can never actually be used and a sample of a finite number of points from the area is necessary. The points in the sample then become the units of association, and the coefficient of areal association is calculated from the pairs of values of the two variables taken at these points.

The fact that a sample is used means that the results are subject to sampling error. This is due to the fact that, since only a portion of the population is being used, there will be a difference between the value of the *sample coefficient of areal association* and the value of the population coefficient of areal association. Fortunately, hypotheses can be tested to determine the probability of the sampling error having a given range of values in any particular case (see Chapter IX).

Since areally continuous variables are being used, the selection of such a sample is a comparatively simple process. Several methods are possible, but the most common procedure is to start by placing an overlay with a numbered grid system on a map or section of a globe showing the area under consideration. The grid should be fine enough so that each numbered point represents a very small unit area. An appropriate number of these points are then selected for the sample. This is accomplished by using a table of random numbers.[1] The points selected are those whose number on the grid corresponds to a number in the table. The values of the two variables at these points become the observations that are used for the computation of the sample coefficient of areal association. One of the advantages of this method of measuring areal association is that the investigator is at liberty to choose any sample size, p, which he believes is appropriate.

One feature of these procedures which is sometimes overlooked is that the selection of control points for the construction of surfaces, and the selection of sample points for measuring the degree of association between surfaces, are entirely independent processes. Studies have been published[2] where the control points were used as the sample points in order to show data for certain political subdivisions. The disadvantage of this approach is that the sample points have not been randomly selected and, therefore, precise tests of hypotheses cannot be employed to analyze the sample coefficient of areal association.

Measures of Areal Association

After the selection of the appropriate macrogeographic variables and the drawing of a random sample, the actual computation of a coefficient of areal association is a routine procedure. Any of the measures used in ordinary linear correlation analysis can be employed. However, the name *coefficient of areal association*[3], ca, will be reserved for the coefficient that is calculated by using the product-moment formula or the method of least squares.[4]

Rank correlation procedures also are applicable when areal distributions are being analyzed. The *coefficient of rank areal association* will be represented by the symbol ca_s when Spearman's measure is used and by ca_k when Kendall's coefficient is employed.

---

[1] Tables of random numbers appear in many statistics text books. The random numbers used for the examples in this study are from the table in Dixon and Massy [27], pp. 366-370.

[2] Warntz [118], pp. 43-102.

[3] Since the coefficient of areal association will be calculated from sample values small letters are used in the symbol. The population coefficient of areal association will be represented by the symbol CA.

[4] The equivalence of these two methods is demonstrated in Mills [68], p. 227n.

Each of these measures has certain advantages and limitations. The greatest asset of least squares is that it is the only one of these methods in which an estimating equation is obtained, and the constants in such an equation can be useful statistics.[5] However, the calculation of ca is based on the assumptions that the values of the variables are normally distributed about their mean and that the deviations are normally distributed about the line of regression. Departures from these assumptions reduce the significance of the result but do not destroy the usefulness of the measure.

This problem can be circumvented by using ca_s or ca_k. Coefficients of rank areal association are non-parametric; they require no assumptions about the nature of the population distributions. Another advantage of ca_s is that its value is extremely easy to calculate. However, there are difficulties associated with ca_s when there are tied ranks; and in certain situations, the significance of a value of ca_s cannot be properly tested.[6] Since areal association always is measured for samples, this latter difficulty is a great disadvantage of ca_s. On the other hand, while a complete range of inference procedures are available for ca_k, the computation of a value of ca_k can be a laborious process if the sample consists of even a moderately large number of items.

Thus, ca usually is the most satisfactory measure of areal association. In addition, inference procedures have been developed which reduce the effect of the lack of normality of the population distributions. These methods will be discussed in the next chapter. Formulas for computing and testing the coefficients of rank areal association will not be given here, but they can be found in many statistics texts.

Although this discussion has been restricted to the case of two variable rectilinear correlation, all measures of correlation can be applied to the study of areal distributions. When several surfaces are being compared, and a random sample of positions has been drawn, ordinary coefficients of multiple and partial correlation can be employed. Similarly, if the graph of the sample values of two areal variables does not warrant the assumption of linearity, the techniques of curvilinear correlation analysis can be used. Once again, the methods for computing and testing the values of these measures will not be discussed here since they are readily available.

One feature of all measures of correlation is that the significance of their values depends on the size of the sample. Unfortunately, this often has been ignored when these techniques have been applied to geographic data. McCarty and his associates ([66], pp. 13-14) have suggested that, for the United States, states might be better units of association than counties since the coefficient of variation is less for state areas than for county areas. Such reasoning completely ignores the 3000 degrees of freedom that will be gained by using counties instead of states. Of course, if possible, discrete areal variables and non-random samples should not be used at all.

---

[5] Examples of the usefulness of the constants in the least squares estimating equation for two areal variables can be found in Stewart and Warntz [96, 97] and Warntz [114, 115].

[6] Mills [68], pp. 315-316.

This feature also is important when one considers the number of variables to be used in a multiple areal association problem. Frequently, two basic independent variables can be combined into one derived independent variable. The resulting gain of one degree of freedom may increase the significance of the value of the coefficient of multiple areal association, even though that value may be reduced by the change in variables.

Some Applications of Areal Association

Most of the studies of areal association which have been published have involved the relationship between two discrete variables or between one discrete variable and potential. Studies of the latter type have served to demonstrate the importance of potential as a macroscopic indication of the areal pattern of many phenomena. Several examples of variables which have been shown to be closely related to potential were mentioned previously (see Chapter V). Coefficients of areal association were obtained in each of these cases. Since non-random samples were used and one variable was not areally continuous, these results are not subject to precise tests of hypotheses. However, the values of the coefficients are meaningful as rough indications of the degree of the relationship between the two variables.

Many of the dependent variables in these problems were basically economic phenomena, so income potential often was used as the independent variable. A 1959 income potential map[7] for the United States is shown as *Figure 38*. Note the basic similarity of the contour pattern between this map and the map of potential of population *(Figure 20)*. The major peak of income potential is at New York City, with subsidiary peaks at Chicago, Boston, Los Angeles, Cleveland, San Francisco and Seattle. A large increase in the number of control points used in the calculation of the values for this map probably would reveal additional minor peaks at other urban centers. However, these peaks would rise so little above the surrounding values that their locations would not be important nationally, although they might have regional importance.

Once the pattern of both potential of population and income potential for the United States has been established, the degree of areal association between certain variables and potential can be examined. Relationships between potential and discrete areal variables can be grouped into four categories. The first of these includes all cases where the dependent variable is a density distribution. In this field Stewart and Warntz ([95], p. 176) have investigated the relationship between several density distributions and income potential for the United States in 1950. They used the 48 states as the units of association and based the coefficients of areal association on least squares lines fitted to the logarithms of the variables. Some of their results are listed below for the following dependent variables (where n is the symbol for the number of degrees of freedom):

Income density	$ca = 0.87, \; n = 47$
Road density	$ca = 0.86, \; n = 47$
Telephone wire density	$ca = 0.85, \; n = 47$
Railroad track density	$ca = 0.86, \; n = 47$

---

[7] The income data used were the 1959 estimates of "Effective Buying Income" given in *Sales Management* [80], pp. 60–379.

132

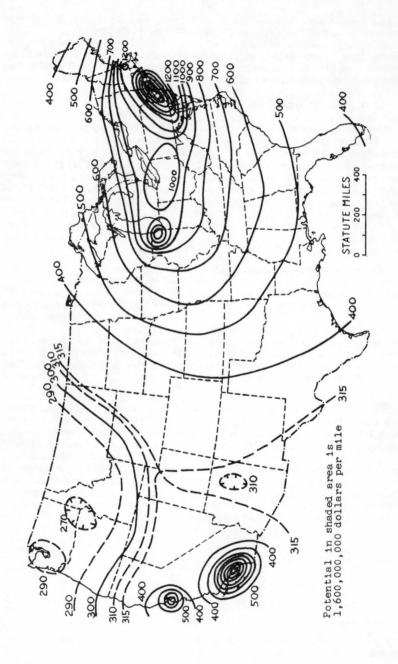

STATUTE MILES

0   200   400

Potential in shaded area is
1,600,000,000 dollars per mile

FIGURE 38.—United States—Income Potential, 1959

Even though these results cannot be precisely tested, it is apparent that a significant degree of association exists in each case.

Stewart and Warntz ([95], p. 177) have examined also the extent of the inverse relationship between income potential and the area of certain sub-divisions within the United States in 1950. Once again, a logarithmic estimating equation was used and some of the results are as follows:

Federal Reserve District areas	$ca = -0.94,$	$n = 11$
Wholesale dry goods market areas	$ca = -0.79,$	$n = 45$
State areas	$ca = -0.85,$	$n = 47$
Mean county area per state	$ca = -0.84,$	$n = 47$
Mean farm area per state	$ca = -0.74,$	$n = 47$

The third category of studies deals with the investigation of the areal distribution of price. For certain commodities, prices received by producers are closely related to potential. The following results were obtained when 1958 and 1959 prices were compared to 1959 income potential, with states again being used as the units of association:

Wheat	$ca_s = 0.67,$	$n = 47$
Crude petroleum	$ca = 0.65,$	$n = 26$
Hay	$ca = 0.59,$	$n = 47$

Finally, relationships between many additional economic variables and income potential in the United States have been examined. With states used as the units of association and logarithmic estimating equations employed, some of the results that have been obtained are as follows:[8]

Ratio of the number of business failures to the total number of businesses, 1949-1951 vs. 1950 income potential	$ca = 0.69,\ n = 40$
Value of farm land and buildings per acre, 1954 vs. 1956 income potential	$ca = 0.76,\ n = 47$
Number of auto fatalities per registered vehicle, 1949-1951 vs. 1950 income potential	$ca = -0.80,\ n = 47$

The last of these examples is particularly interesting because the large negative value of the coefficient of areal association is contrary to the popular belief that the probability of being in a fatal automobile accident varies directly with the amount of traffic in a region.

Unfortunately, few studies have been published where associations between continuous areal surfaces were measured. Krumbein [58] examined the relationship among thicknesses of several geologic features in the mid-western United

---

[8] The first and last of these results are from Stewart and Warntz [95], p. 180.

States. Warntz [116, 118] investigated the relationship between areal patterns of supply and demand for several commodities in the United States. He used production potentials[9] to measure supply and income potential to indicate demand or accessibility to market. Thus, the coefficient of areal association can be thought of as an index of the "market orientation of production". Warntz [116, 118] used non-random samples with states as the units of association and potentials computed for the mid-1940's. His results are given below for the following dependent variables:

Wheat production potential	$ca_s = -0.26$, $n = 47$
Onion production potential	$ca_s = 0.40$, $n = 47$
Strawberry production potential	$ca_s = 0.59$, $n = 47$
Potato production potential	$ca_s = 0.77$, $n = 47$
Ice Cream production potential	$ca_s = 0.99$, $n = 47$

This type of analysis has been extended to other commodities by the present author. As examples,

Log 1954 shorn wool production potential vs.
   log 1965 income potential $ca = -0.45$, $n = 47$

1950 corn production potential vs.
   1950 income potential $ca_s = 0.46$, $n = 47$

Thus, the coefficient of areal association can be used to indicate the degree to which the location of the production of a commodity is influenced by the areal distribution of income.

This type of analysis can be carried one step further to investigate the areal patterns for the various stages in the life of a commodity from the production of raw material to the demand for the finished item. Three of these stages for two resources copper and petroleum, will be analyzed here as examples of this process. All data are for the late 1950's in the United States. As the first step, four potential distributions were computed. The distribution of crude petroleum production potential features a huge plateau in the Texas-Oklahoma-Lousiana region with individual peaks at the locations of the major oil fields within this region. There is a subsidiary peak in California and the lowest value is located at the northern tip of Maine.

The peak of the distribution of petroleum refining potential is also in the Texas-Oklahoma-Louisiana region. However, in this case, there are important subsidiary peaks in New Jersey, Illinois, and California. The lowest values are found in northwestern Washington, and the tips of Maine and Florida. There is also a minor pit in Arizona.

The distribution of copper mine production potential has its major peak in Arizona with an additional very minor peak in northern Michigan. Once again, the

---

[9] A production potential is simply potential of population with the amount of the commodity that is produced used as the population.

west values are found at the northern tip of Maine. The distribution of copper melting potential has the same topological features as copper mine production potential.

For both resources, 1959 income potential was used as an indication of accessibility to market. Now, coefficients of areal association can be used to indicate how much the distribution of the intermediate stage (petroleum refining and copper smelting) is influenced by the areal patterns of the production of the raw material and accessibility to market.

The next step in the process was the selection of a random sample of 25 positions. Coefficients of areal association then were computed, based on the values of the variables at these 25 sample points, with the following results:

Copper mine production potential vs.
    income potential $ca = -0.68$

Copper smelting potential vs.
    copper mine production potential $ca = 0.98$

Copper smelting potential vs.
    income potential $ca = -0.63$

Crude petroleum production potential vs.
    income potential $ca = -0.45$

Petroleum refining potential vs.
    crude petroleum production potential $ca = 0.34$

Petroleum refining potential vs.
    income potential $ca = 0.60$

These results show that there is a definite negative relationship between the areal pattern of the production of the raw material and income potential for both copper and petroleum. However, in the case of copper, the smelting process apparently is performed near the mines while the location of petroleum refining seems to be influenced by the areal patterns of both the oil wells and income.

The influence exerted by both crude petroleum production potential and income potential on the distribution of petroleum refining potential can be measured by using a *coefficient of multiple areal association* $(ma_{1.23\ldots v}$, where v is the number of variables in the problem, with petroleum refining potential as the dependent variable. For this example, $ma_{1.23}=0.91$. This provides additional evidence that the areal distribution of petroleum refining is influenced by the location of both raw material and market. A similar measure for copper is unnecessary since almost all of the variation in the areal pattern of copper smelting potential has been "explained" by the distribution of copper mine production potential. Of course, this type of analysis can be extended to other commodities and to any number of stages for each commodity.

Since these coefficients of areal association were based on a random sample, the values are subject to further analysis involving tests of hypotheses. Such tests will be discussed in the following chapter.

CHAPTER IX
AREAL INFERENCE AND ESTIMATION

Areal Sampling

Investigators who wish to analyze areal data often will be able to use data for entire populations. Such complete data are available a larger proportion of the time for areal populations than they are for linear populations. Thus, areal sampling, and consequently, procedures of inference and estimation based on sample statistics, play a less important role than their linear counterparts.

Nevertheless, there are some important applications of areal sampling. One already has been mentioned—coefficients of areal association always are computed for samples.

In addition, samples are often used when population data are unwieldy. As an example, the areal distribution of the residences of the members of the Association of American Geographers who live in the United States will be studied later in this chapter. These data are available in the form of an alphabetical list of the 1871 members of the association. [1] To facilitate the analysis of this large number of items, random samples can be drawn from the list.

The remainder of this chapter will be devoted to a discussion of various procedures of inference and estimation designed to test the significance of the values of certain sample statistics.

Ideally, this chapter should contain a description of the sampling distribution of every sample statistic discussed in earlier chapters, all measures of average position, areal dispersion, areal skewness and kurtosis, etc. Then, the significance of all areal sample statistics could be measured. Unfortunately, limitations of space and the introductory nature of this book do not warrant the presentation of the complicated mathematical derivations of most of these distributions. Thus, the remainder of this chapter is merely a brief introduction to the potentially vast subject of areal inference and estimation.

Tests of Sample Coefficients of Areal Association

The procedures of inference and estimation which involve *ca* are the same as those designed for the linear coefficient of correlation. Therefore, these methods merely will be outlined here since more detailed discussions can be found in many statistics texts.

---

[1] The Association of the American Geographers [101], pp. 45-162. This list contains a mixture of home and business addresses, but distances between these are not likely to be large enough to seriously affect subsequent results.

For the random sample of 25 positions that was mentioned in the last chapter, the coefficient of areal association between petroleum refining potential and crude petroleum production potential had a value of 0.34. We now wish to determine whether this sample can be considered to have been drawn from a population with $CA=0$. The first step is to choose arbitrarily a level of significance. This level is the probability of reaching a false conclusion that the observed facts are inconsistent with the null hypothesis that the sample was drawn from a population with $CA=0$. When working with areal data it is advisable to use small probabilities as levels of significance because the individual observed values are not strictly independent. In this study, 0.01 will be used as the level of significance.

There are several methods for testing the hypothesis, depending on the number of items in the sample and the assumptions that are made about the sampling distribution of ca. The sampling distribution of ca varies with the values of CA and p, approaching a normal distribution as p increases. This tendency is much more pronounced for values of CA close to zero. When this normality is assumed, the standard error of ca, which is denoted by SE_{ca}, equals $\frac{1-(CA)^2}{\sqrt{p-1}}$.

For this example, $CA=0$ and $p=25$. Therefore, $SE_{ca}=0.2041$. Then a normal deviate, T, can be calculated from the expression, $T=\frac{ca-CA}{SE_{ca}}$. In this case, $T=1.67$. From a table of areas under the normal curve, it can be seen that a probability of 0.01 corresponds to a value of T of 2.576. Since $1.67 < 2.576$, it must be concluded that the observed facts are not inconsistent with the null hypothesis. There is no reason to believe that the difference between $ca=0.34$ and $CA=0$ is not due to "chance" factors.

Fisher's[2] "z'" distribution is often used for testing the significance of a value of ca because it approaches normality faster than the distribution of ca. However, this difference is negligible when $CA=0$, so z' will not be used in this example.

When p is small (usually, $p \leq 30$) and $CA=0$, Student's "t" distribution should be used. The appropriate statistic is $t=\frac{ca\sqrt{p-2}}{\sqrt{1-(ca)^2}}$ with $p-2$ degrees of freedom. For the example of the coefficient of areal association between petroleum refining potential and crude petroleum production potential, $t=1.73$ and $n=23$. From a table of the values of t, it can be seen that, for $n=23$, a probability of 0.01 corresponds to $t=2.807$. Since $1.73 < 2.807$, it must be concluded, once again, that the observed facts are not inconsistent with the null hypothesis.

Similar procedures can be used to test other values of ca mentioned in Chapter VIII which were computed from random samples. For the coefficient of areal association between petroleum refining potential and income potential, $T=2.95$ and $t=3.63$, so the conclusion is that the observed facts are inconsistent with the null hypothesis and that there is reason to believe that the sample was not drawn from a population with $CA=0$. The same conclusion is reached

[2]Fisher's z' is a logarithmic transformation of ca: $z'=\frac{1}{2}\left[log_e(1+ca)-log_e(1-ca)\right]$.

For a more detailed discussion of z', see Mills [68], pp. 299-302.

when copper smelting potential and copper mine production potential are the variables since $T=4.78$ and $t=21.49$. The null hypothesis also is rejected in the case of the association between copper smelting potential and income potential. Here there is a significant inverse relationship as $T=-3.11$ and $t=-3.93$. It is interesting to note that, for these four examples which were originally presented in Chapter VIII, the use of the normal curve and the t distribution lead to the same conclusions.

There also are procedures for testing the significance of a difference between two sample coefficients of areal association or differences between population and sample values of coefficients of multiple and partial areal association, rank areal association, and curvilinear areal association. These methods are the same as the corresponding methods for linear statistics which are extensively treated in many of the standard books on that subject.

Tests of Sample Arithmetic Mean Centers

Two random samples were selected from the list of residences of members of the Association of American Geographers who live in the United States. The first sample consisted of 11 items. Its arithmetic mean center, s_c was found to be in western Indiana, 132 miles from the arithmetic mean center of the 1960 United States population. The sample standard distance deviation, s_r, was 818 miles. Existing linear methods cannot be used to test the significance of the location of s_c because the sampling distributions of average positions are, themselves, areal distributions. Fortunately, the sampling distribution of s_c approaches the Normal Probability Surface very rapidly so appropriate testing procedures can easily be devised. However, when the size of the sample is small, the Normal Probability Surface is not a satisfactory approximation to the distribution of sample arithmetic mean centers. The corresponding problem in linear statistics was solved by the introduction of the t distribution for samples drawn from normal populations. For the areal case, a univariate areal counterpart of t, which shall be called t_r, can be defined. For a given number of degrees of freedom the proba-

bility distribution of t_r can be computed from the expression, $\dfrac{D_x}{D_c} = \dfrac{1}{\left(1 + \dfrac{t_r^2}{n}\right)^{n+1}}$.

Values for density and volume tables of t_r distributions, corresponding to *Tables 8* and *9* for the Normal Probability Surface, have been calculated by this writer for $n = 1, 2, 3, 4, 5, 10,$ and 25. Unlike the Normal Probability Surface, however, the values in the two tables for a given t_r distribution are not complementary. Not only is t_r analogous to the linear t but the relationship between t_r and the Normal Probability Surface is analogous to the relationship between t and the normal distribution. As $n \rightarrow \infty$, t_r approaches the Normal Probability Surface. It is not necessary for all the tables of t_r that have been compiled to be shown here. The values of t_r for some of the most commonly used levels of significance are shown in *Table 25*.

TABLE 25

VALUES OF t_r

n (Degrees of Freedom)	Level of significance (Probability)								
	0.90	0.70	0.50	0.30	0.20	0.01	0.05	0.02	0.01
1	0.333	0.655	1.000	1.527	2.000	3.000	4.357	7.000	10.000
2	0.329	0.625	0.910	1.285	1.572	2.079	2.635	3.484	4.246
3	0.327	0.615	0.883	1.217	1.458	1.861	2.268	2.838	3.306
4	0.327	0.611	0.870	1.185	1.408	1.764	2.111	2.575	2.938
5	0.326	0.608	0.862	1.167	1.378	1.710	2.025	2.435	2.748
10	0.325	0.603	0.847	1.131	1.321	1.609	1.869	2.188	2.417
25	0.325	0.599	0.838	1.111	1.289	1.553	1.784	2.057	2.248
(Normal Probability Surface) ∞	0.325	0.597	0.833	1.097	1.269	1.517	1.731	1.978	2.146

In this case, the null hypothesis to be tested states that the sample of 11 geographers was drawn from the population of people living in the continental United States in 1960, assuming that this population has a Normal Probability Surface distribution.

The level of significance is, once again, 0.01. This test is based on the use of the standard error of the sample arithmetic mean center, SE_{s_C}, as an estimate of the standard error of the population arithmetic mean center, SE_{S_C}, and S_r is not used, even if its value is known. To make this an unbiased estimate, s_r must be divided by $\sqrt{p-1}$ rather than by $\sqrt{p}$, and the size of the sample relative to the size of population must be considered. Thus, $SE_{s_C} = \frac{s_r}{\sqrt{p-1}} \sqrt{\frac{P-p}{P-1}}$. Therefore,[3] $SE_{s_C} = \frac{818 \text{ miles}}{\sqrt{11-1}} = 259 \text{ miles}$. Then, $t_r = \frac{r_{Ss}}{SE_{s_C}}$ where r_{Ss} is the distance between S_C and s_C. Thus, $t_r = \frac{132 \text{ miles}}{259 \text{ miles}} = 0.51$. The number of degrees of freedom, n, is governed by the relationship, $n=p-1$. From *Table 25* it can be seen that a probability of 0.01 corresponds to $t_r = 2.417$ when $n=10$. Since $0.51 < 2.417$, the conclusion is that the observed result is not inconsistent with the hypothesis. There is no reason to belive that the sample of 11 geographers was not drawn from the

---

[3]Since $P > 178,000,000$ and $p=11$, the correction factor of $\sqrt{\frac{P-p}{P-1}}$ can be assumed to equal one without any loss of accuracy. In fact, with such a large population, this assumption would be most reasonable even if there were several thousand items in the sample.

1960 population of the continental United States. The difference between 0.51 and 2.417 is large enough to support this conclusion even though it is known that the distribution of this population is not too close to the Normal Probability Surface.

A second random sample, consisting of 100 items, was selected from the list of geographer's residences. This was done in order to illustrate the effect of sample size on testing procedures. For this sample, s_c was in central Illinois, 95 miles from the location of S_c for the 1960 population of the United States, and $s_r = 760$ miles.

When p is large the Normal Probability Surface so nearly resembles t_r that it may be substituted as a very close approximation to t_r. The rapidity with which t_r approaches the Normal Probability Surface can be seen by examining the values in the columns of *Table 25*.

For this test, one can make use of the fact that the value of the population standard distance deviation is known $(S_r = 839 \ miles)$. The standard error of the population arithmetic mean center can then be calculated from the expression,

$SE_{S_c} = \dfrac{S_r}{\sqrt{P}}$ and the deviate of the Normal Probability Surface distribution, T_r,

is equal to $\dfrac{r_{Ss}}{SE_{S_c}}$. Thus, $SE_{S_c} = \dfrac{839 \ miles}{\sqrt{100}} = 83.9 \ miles$ and $T_r = \dfrac{95 \ miles}{83.9 \ miles} =$

1.13. From *Table 9* it can be seen that a probability of 0.01 corresponds to $T_r = 2.146$. As $1.13 < 2.146$, there is no reason to believe that this sample was not drawn from the 1960 population of the continental United States. Since p is large, T_r could be used even if the value of S_r were not known for the sample of 100

geographers. In such an instance, $SE_{S_c} = \dfrac{760 \ miles}{\sqrt{100-1}} = 76.4 \ miles$ and $T_r =$

$\dfrac{95 \ miles}{76.4 \ miles} = 1.24$. Since $1.24 < 2.146$ the conclusion is still that the observed result is not inconsistent with the hypothesis.

The data from these two samples of geographers also can be used to test the hypothesis that these samples were drawn from the same population. Of course, in this case it is known that both samples were drawn from the same list. Nevertheless, the test will be performed in order to illustrate the procedures which are involved. The distance between the two sample arithmetic mean centers, represented by r_{ss}, was 138 miles. The standard error of the distance can be

calculated from the formula, $SE_{r_{ss}} = \sqrt{\dfrac{(p_1+p_2)\left(p_1 s_{r_1}^2 + p_2 s_{r_2}^2\right)}{p_1 p_2 (p_1+p_2-2)}}$. Then, $t_r = \dfrac{r_{ss}}{SE_{r_{ss}}}$

where $n = p_1 + p_2 - 2$. Treating the group of 11 geographers as sample "1" and the group of 100 as sample "2", $SE_{r_{ss}} = 246 \ miles$ and $t_r = 0.56$ with $n = 109$. Since n is large, T_r may be used as a close approximation to t_r. Thus, $T_r = 0.56$. Using 0.01 as the level of significance, there is no reason to reject the null hypothesis.

This test should be used only when S_c is not known. When S_c is known, more meaningful results can be obtained by testing each s_c against S_c. In this case, both samples were actually drawn from a population of 1,871 geographers, and S_c really was not known, although previous tests showed that the samples could be considered to have been drawn from the entire 1960 population of the continental United States.

Several tests have indicated that the areal distribution of the residences of the members of the Association of American Geographers who lived in the continental United States in 1960 was not significantly different from the areal pattern of the residences of all people living in that area in 1960. Of course, it is important to remember that these conclusions depend on an assumed population distribution and on the arbitrary selection of a level of significance. However, for the tests shown in this section, the probability of the observed result being due to chance was greater than 0.2 in each case so that the same conclusions would have been reached for all reasonable levels of significance. Moreover, when p is large (100 or more) the difference between the population distribution and the Normal Probability Surface has only a slight effect on the results of these tests.

Confidence Limits

In the previous section statistical tests of hypotheses were used to examine the relationship between the distribution of two samples of geographers and the distribution of population within the continental United States. As stated, these samples were actually drawn from a list of 1,871 geographers, with an unknown population arithmetic mean center. Instead of comparing the sample to the national population, we now seek an estimate of the location of this unknown S_C. The method that will be employed is a simple areal counterpart of the linear technique of interval estimation based on confidence limits. For areal distributions, the interval becomes a circle with s_C as center and radius equal to $t_r SE_{s_C}$ (SE_{s_C} is used instead of SE_{S_C} if the value of S_r is known). The value of t_r that is used is the one which corresponds to the selected confidence coefficient.

For the sample of 11 geographers, S_r is unknown, $s_r = 818$ *miles*, $P = 1871$, and $p = 11$. Thus, $SE_{s_C} = \dfrac{818 \ miles}{\sqrt{11-1}} \sqrt{\dfrac{1871-11}{1871-1}} = 258 \ miles$. Choosing a confidence coefficient of 0.99, $t_r = 2.417$ since $n = p-1 = 10$ (See *Table 25*). Therefore, the radius of the circle of estimation, $t_r SE_{s_C}$, is 624 miles. Now one can make a statement that the population arithmetic mean center is located within a circle whose center is the sample arithmetic mean center in western Indiana and whose radius is 624 miles. Such a statement must be either true or false. However, if a very large number of random samples of 11 were drawn from the same population with a Normal Probability Surface distribution, and a similar statement was made for each, approximately 99% of these statements would be true. Hence, the larger the confidence coefficient (or probability coefficient since it does represent a probability), the more "confidence" one has that his statement, based on the results of only one sample, is true. Of course, an increase in the value of this coefficient also serves to increase the radius of the circle of estimation, making the estimate of S_C less precise. Thus, in a given situation, the investigator must decide which is more desirable—a small radius for the circle of estimation or a great amount of confidence in the estimating statement.

For the second sample, consisting of 100 items, $s_r = 760$ miles and SE_{s_C} = $\dfrac{760 \ miles}{\sqrt{100-1}} \sqrt{\dfrac{1871-100}{1871-1}} = 74.3 \ miles$. Since p is large, the Normal Probability

Surface can be used as an approximation to the t_γ distribution. Again using a probability coefficient of 0.99, $T_\gamma = 2.146$ (see *Table 9*) and $T_\gamma SE_{S_C} = 159$ *miles*. The statement of estimation is that S_C is located within a circle whose center is s_C in central Illinois and whose radius is 159 miles.

The circles of estimation based on both of these samples are shown as *Figure 39*. This map clearly illustrates the advantage of using a larger sample in order to obtain more precise estimates of S_C. It is also interesting to note that the arithmetic mean center of the entire population of the continental United States in 1960 is located within both of these circles of estimation. This provides still another indication that the samples of geographers can be considered to have been drawn from the total human population of the country.

The procedures for obtaining interval estimates of population coefficients of areal association from sample results are the same as the corresponding methods in linear statistics.

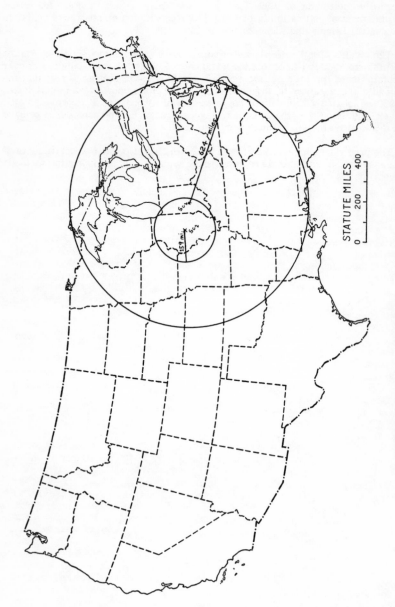

FIGURE 39.—Circles of Estimation of S_c for the Population of United States Geographers Based on Samples of 11 and 100 Geographers

CHAPTER X
FINAL REMARKS

Summary

Almost all contemporary research studies in the social sciences and business contain at least some statistical or mathematical analysis of quantitative data. In most fields the researcher has a vast array of well-developed techniques and methodological tools at his disposal which he can use in his analysis of these data.

As an example, consider the case of the economist who wishes to study a series of time-ordered observations. Virtually all statistics texts and many works in economics contain large sections dealing with procedures for the statistical analysis of time series. These sections usually include methods for analyzing trend, seasonal movements and cyclical fluctuations; index number theory and practice; and correlation of time series. Many of these techniques are so well established that there is a fairly high degree of uniformity among the various books treating this subject, with respect both to content and notation. Thus, the prospective investigator can read one or two of these works and become familiar with a sizable number of basic techniques for the statistical analysis of time distributions. Of course, this methodology is neither complete nor perfect. The large number of theoretical articles devoted to this topic which have appeared recently in the leading statistical and econometric journals indicate that many additions to, and revisions of, the basic methods are still needed.

Nevertheless, a researcher concerned with the statistical analysis of time distributions can find, in a single source, a basic, comprehensive, internally consistent set of tools for performing this type of analysis. In addition, the great amount of constructive criticism of the existing quantitative methods for time series analysis indicates that many economists are vitally concerned with improving and supplementing the existing methodology. Such activity also implies that these economists recognize the importance of developing a satisfactory system for the statistical analysis of time distributions.

If, instead, the researcher were interested in the statistical analysis of areal distributions, he could find no such single methodological source or widespread interest. He could, perhaps, find little bits of information in articles and books dealing with Location Theory, Regional Science, Social Physics, and Centrography. These sources provide methods for analyzing certain particular situations. However, there is little uniformity, either in content or notation, among these studies. Moreover, the sum of all of the studies still falls far short of providing a basic comprehensive set of tools for analyzing areal distributions.

This work has been an attempt to partially fill this void by outlining a simple, integrated, and internally consistent system of statistical analysis for areal distributions. It is hoped that this represents a start toward the goal which the analysis of areal distributions should reach—a position in the social sciences roughly corresponding to the position occupied by the analysis of time series. It is also hoped that the internally consistent notation system proposed in this study may serve as a unifying force which will facilitate comprehension of future literature related to this topic. A start in this direction has alread been made as Warntz has indicated he will use many of these symbols i several forthcoming publications.

The methods outlined in this study are based on a definition of an are; distribution as having one fundamental variable—distance. Applications bivariate statistical theory to the analysis of areal distribution, although ofte useful, are limited by the choice of a coordinate system and by the assumptic of a plane surface.

This definition of an areal distribution led to the construction of a syste1 of areal moments based on the shortest great circle distance between two point on the earth's surface. These moments, in turn, provided the basis for th development of several descriptive measures of average position, dispersic and kurtosis. In addition, some descriptive measures not directly based c areal moments were discussed. Among these were the measures of are; skewness.

More meaningful comparisons of distribution can often be made when certa' absolute standards are available for reference. In linear statistics the norm; curve of error is frequently used as such a standard. Several possible mod« surfaces were mentioned in this study but the three most important ones ar the Normal Probability Surface, the Circular Uniform Surface and the Mea Deviation Surface. Values of certain measures of dispersion based on thes models were calculated in order to provide additional standards for comparisor The Normal Probability Surface is also the areal counterpart of the norm; curve and, therefore, it is most useful in problems of areal inference an estimation—particularly when large samples are used. For certain sma. samples, the t_r distribution, which is the areal equivalent of Student's t dis tribution, was introduced.

Finally, two subjects, directly related to the statistical analysis of area distributions, which have been developed in previous literature, were briefl reviewed in this study. These are nearest neighbor analysis and areal asso ciation.

In conjunction with this theoretical approach, several applications wer« presented. These included a quantitative examination of the areal patterns o population in seven nations, an analysis of the demographic history of th United States, and an investigation of the areal distribution of two commoditie: within the United States at various stages in the production cycle from th raw material to market. Although the applications in this work have com« largely from the field of demographs, the methods that have been discussed ar« applicable to the analysis of any phenomena distributed over an area.

Once again it must be emphasized that the methods and applications tha have been developed and discussed in the previous chapters are based on ; macrogeographic approach. Actual decisions can rarely be based solely on th values of these statistical measures. However, these values do provide a usefu

quantitative first approximation upon which business and planning decisions can
be based. Macrogeographic studies often will provide insights and reveal relationships which no amount of detailed local study could uncover.[1]

Future Research

Finally, it is intended that this study represent a beginning rather than an
end. It is hoped that more individuals, particularly geographers, will become
interested in narrowing the gaps between statistics and geography and between
economics and geography.

In the field of statistical analysis of areal distributions there are many
avenues open to extensive future research. More empirical research is clearly
needed. Empirical research based on some of the methods discussed in this study
has already resulted in the formulation of theories and the demonstration of
regularities dealing with the distribution of income, rural population, migration,
administrative areas, mental health, political and economic relationships among
nations, etc. These methods also are currently being used as vital tools in the
formulation of a theory of the areal distribution of home and school residences
of college students in the United States and in a macrogeographic investigation
of the political and demographic history of the world.[2]

There surely are many other significant and important macrogeographic
relationships that remain to be shown as the results of future research. For
example, more empirical demographic research may lead to the formulation
of general theories dealing with the areal distribution of population or with
the history of population growth. Also, investigation of the areal patterns of
various phenomena over the same area may reveal previously unknown regularities, particularly if many areas and time periods are examined.

---

[1] O.M. Miller, Assistant Director of the American Geographical Society, has composed the
following short poem describing this point of view. It originally appeared in Stewart and
Warntz [95] , p. 184.

Geography,
In small degree,
Collects
The facts that be
On land and sea;
Expects
But little thought,
Nor is it sought

Geography,
In large degree,
Is thus
The gift to see
Not thee and me
But us,
Summed up with grace
In mass and space.

This view of seeing "not thee and me, but us" has been one of the fundamental principles
of this work.

[2] Both of these studies have been conducted by Warntz at the American Geographical Society.
The results will appear in future publications as well as in Warntz [113] , [114].

An illustration of this is the relationship between the arithmetic mea
center of population and the arithmetic mean center of corn production in th
United States for the past two centuries. The closeness of this relationshi
suggests that the areal distribution of corn production has been influenced mor
by the distribution of population and less by the soil and climate factors of
"natural corn belt" than is generally recognized in the current geographi
literature.

The techniques of production stage analysis based on areal associatio
can be used to examine the geographic pattern of industry. More empirica
research of this type could yield quantitative estimates of the influence c
location of market, raw materials, and other factors on the location of variou
industrial facilities. Generalizations about certain products which tend to hav
similar areal patterns all the way from raw material to market may also be
result of this avenue of investigation. This type of analysis, when supplemente
by local information, may prove to be quite useful for location planning i
business.

In addition, there are several opportunities for future theoretical researc
to increase the number of tools available for analyzing areal distributions. Fo
example, Warntz in a study as yet unpublished has indicated that the coefficient o
areal assoccation can be considered to have three components. Unfortunately, n
one has yet indicated how the effect of each of these sources of variation can b
measured. The author of this study has conducted some preliminary research a
the American Geographical Society in an effort to measure the effect of one c
these components, topological variation. However, even if this research prove
to be successful, only a small part of the question will be answered and muc
additional study of areal variation will be necessary.

Furthermore, there will always be a place for useful new measures an
methods and new types of applications for the existing techniques.

In the field of areal sampling and inference, little has been accomplished
The sampling distribution of only one of the measures of average position, dis
persion, skewness and kurtosis discussed in this work has been described. Whil
this knowledge of the sampling distribution of the arithmetic mean center permit
much useful testing of hypotheses, more theoretical research is obviously needed
Descriptions of the sampling distribution of sample median centers, harmoni
mean centers, standard distance deviations, mean distance deviations, genera
mean distance deviations, and harmonic mean distance deviations would be par
ticularly valuable contributions. Such contributions, if accomplished, would, c
course, permit many additional and useful tests of hypotheses and estimates o
areal parameters.

If such additional research is undertaken, the analysis of areal distribution
may reach the stage of the analysis of time distributions—with a well develope
statistical methodology at a researcher's disposal. Of course, there will alway
be problems and difficulties to interest the theoretical researcher, just as ther
are today in the field of time series analysis.

If such a situation should exist, the goal of this study will have bee
realized—the geographer will have at his disposal a simple, internally consisten
system of statistical methods that has been designed to meet the specific needs o
his profession.

APPENDIX A.

LIST OF SYMBOLS USED IN THIS STUDY SPECIFICALLY FOR THE ANALYSIS OF AREAL DISTRIBUTIONS

Many other symbols which are used in
their conventional or familiar
sense are not listed in
this Appendix.

A	: area.
a	: effectively settled area.
A_c	: arithmetic mean center of area.
a_c	: arithmetic mean center of effectively settled area.
A_i	: area of class i.
α	: any real number.
β_2	: a measure of areal kurtosis (same symbol for both population and sample values).
c	: location of the minimum value of the nth root of the nth areal moment.
CA	: population coefficient of areal association.
ca	: sample coefficient of areal association.
CAk	: population value of Kendall's coefficient of rank areal association.
ca_k	: sample value of Kendall's coefficient of rank areal association.
CA_s	: population value of Spearman's coefficient of rank areal association.
ca_s	: sample value of Spearman's coefficient of rank areal association.
D_A	: average density over area A.
D_a	: average density over effectively settled area a.
D_c	: density at a specified average position.
D_x	: density at a specified distance from a specified average position.

E	: demographic energy.
G_c	: population geometric mean center.
g_c	: sample geometric mean center.
G_r	: population geometric mean distance deviation.
g_r	: sample geometric mean distance deviation.
Γ	: gamma function.
H_c	: population harmonic mean center.
h_c	: sample harmonic mean center.
H_P	: population general harmonic mean distance deviation.
h_p	: sample general harmonic mean distance deviation.
H_r	: population harmonic mean distance deviation.
h_r	: sample harmonic mean distance deviation.
i	: a class of an areal frequency distribution, or the contro point of that class.
j	: a position or point on an area.
K	: population measure of areal kurtosis with a limited range o values.
k	: sample measure of areal kurtosis with a limited range o values.
M'_n at j	: population n^{th} areal moment at j.
m'_n at j	: sample n^{th} areal moment at j.
M_n	: population n^{th} areal moment at S_c.
m_n	: sample n^{th} areal moment at s_c.
M'_1 at j	: population mean covergence distance at j.
m'_1 at j	: sample mean convergence distance at j.
$\sqrt[-1]{M'_{-1}}$ at j	: population reciprocal mean distance deviation at j.
$\sqrt[-1]{m'_{-1}}$ at j	: sample reciprocal mean distance deviation at j.
$\sqrt{M'_2}$ at j	: population root-mean-square distance deviation at j.

$\sqrt{m_2'}$ at j	:	sample root-mean-square distance deviation at j.
M_2 or S_r^2	:	population distance variance.
m_2 or s_r^2	:	sample distance variance.
MD_c	:	population median center.
md_c	:	sample median center.
MD_P	:	population general mean distance deviation.
md_P	:	sample general mean distance deviation.
MD_r	:	population mean distance deviation.
md_r	:	sample mean distance deviation.
MO_c	:	population modal center.
mo_c	:	sample modal center.
$MA_{1.23\ldots v}$	:	population coefficient of multiple areal association.
$ma_{1.23\ldots v}$	:	sample coefficient of multiple areal association.
N	:	number of classes in an areal frequency distribution.
n	:	any integer--used to indicate the exponent of distance used in an areal moment.
n	:	degrees of freedom
P	:	the number of items in a population.
p	:	the number of items in a sample.
p_i	:	the number of items in class i, the frequency of class i.
P_x	:	population within a specified distance from a specified average position.
PC_{ru}	:	population percentile distance deviation.
pc_{ru}	:	sample percentile distance deviation.
PD_r	:	population most probable distance.
pd_r	:	sample most probable distance.
PD_x	:	value of the probability density function at a specified distance from a specified average position.

PE_r	:	population probable error.
pe_r	:	sample probable error.
r	:	distance.
r_A	:	radius of A when A is assumed to be circular.
r_a	:	radius of a when a is assumed to be circular.
r_{AP}	:	distance between S_c and A_c.
r_{Ap}	:	distance between s_c and A_c.
r_{aP}	:	distance between S_c and a_c.
r_{ap}	:	distance between s_c and a_c.
r_{cj}	:	distance between c and j.
r_H	:	radius of hexagon.
r_{ij}	:	distance between j and the control point of class i.
r_{jx}	:	distance between j and x.
R_N	:	ratio of the observed arithmetic mean distance to N^{th} nearest neighbor to the expected arithmetic mean distance to N^{th} nearest neighbor for a random distribution.
r_N	:	distance between x and its Nth nearest neighbor.
$\bar{r}_N$	:	arithmetic mean distance to N^{th} nearest neighbor.
r_{SO}	:	distance between S_c and MO_c.
r_{Ss}	:	distance between S_c and s_c.
r_{ss}	:	distance between two sample arithmetic mean centers.
r_x	:	distance between a specified average position and x.
$\bar{\rho}_n$	:	arithmetic mean distance to N^{th} nearest neighbor for an infinitely large randomly distributed population.
S_c	:	population arithmetic mean center.
s_c	:	sample arithmetic mean center.
S_P	:	population general standard distance deviation.
s_p	:	sample general standard distance deviation.

S_P^2	: population general distance variance.
s_P^2	: sample general distance variance.
S_r	: population standard distance deviation.
s_r	: sample standard distance deviation.
S_r^2 or M_2	: population distance variance.
s_r^2 or m_2	: sample distance variance.
SE_{ca}	: standard error of ca.
SE_{S_c}	: standard error of S_c.
SE_{s_c}	: standard error of s_c.
$SE_{r_{ss}}$	: standard error of r_{ss}.
SK_A	: population measure of areal skewness based on total area.
sk_A	: sample measure of areal skewness based on total area.
SK_a	: population measure of areal skewness based on effectively settled area.
sk_a	: sample measure of areal skewness based on effectively settled area.
SK_P	: population measure of areal skewness based solely on population.
sk_p	: sample measure of areal skewness based solely on population.
T	: normal deviate.
T_r	: Normal Probability Surface deviate.
t	: ratio of a normally distributed variable to the square root of an independently distributed estimate of the variance of that variable.
t_r	: ratio of a Normal Probability Surface distributed variable to the square root of an independently distributed estimate of the distance variance of that variable.
u	: percentage of the population or sample.
V	: potential of population.
v	: number of variables in an multiple areal association problem.

154

V_c	: peak potential, the potential of population at H_c.
V_i	: potential of population at the control point of class i.
V_j	: potential of population at j.
V_M	: mean potential.
V_x	: potential of population at x.
VR_c	: population variance center.
vr_c	: sample variance center.
W	: population distance range.
w	: sample distance range.
x	: an item, or the location of that item.
z'	: a logarithmic transformation of ca.
III_c	: population third moment center.
3_c	: sample third moment center.
III_r	: population third moment distance deviation.
3_r	: sample third moment distance deviation.
IV_c	: population fourth moment center.
4_c	: sample fourth moment center.
IV_r	: population fourth moment distance deviation.
4_r	: sample fourth moment distance deviation.
$-II_c$	: population inverse second moment center.
-2_c	: sample inverse second moment center.
$-II_r$	: population inverse second moment distance deviation.
-2_r	: sample inverse second moment distance deviation

APPENDIX B.
DEMONSTRATION OF BIAS DUE TO GROUPING
IN THE CALCULATION OF POSITIVE AREAL MOMENTS

(Based on the distribution shown in *Figure 3b*)

When $n \geqq 2$:

When x_1, x_2, x_3, x_4 are assumed to be grouped at i, $(M_n'$ at $j) = \dfrac{\sum\limits_{1=1}^{N} \left(p_i \, r_{ij}^{\,n} \right)}{P} = \dfrac{\sum\limits_{i=1}^{1} \left(4a^n \right)}{4} = a^n$.

The true value of M_n' at j is found when the observations are not grouped:

$(M_n'$ at $j) = \dfrac{\sum\limits_{x=1}^{P} \left(r_{jx}^{\,n} \right)}{P} = \dfrac{\sum\limits_{x=1}^{4} \left(r_{jx}^{\,n} \right)}{4} = \dfrac{(a+b)^n + (a-b)^n + 2 \left(\sqrt{a^2+b^2} \right)^n}{4}$

Since $a > o$ and $n \geqq 2$

$(a+b)^n + (a-b)^n > 2a^n$.

Therefore, $(M_n'$ at $j) > \dfrac{2a^n + 2 \sqrt{a^2+b^2}^{\,n}}{4}$

Since $a > o$ and $b > o$

$2 \left(\sqrt{a^2+b^2} \right)^n > 2a^n$.

Therefore, $(M_n'$ at $j) > \dfrac{2a^n + 2a^n}{4}$.

Therefore, $(M_n'$ at $j) > a^n$.

Thus, M_n' calculated from grouped data understates the true value when $n \geqq 2$.

When $n=1$:

When x_1, x_2, x_3, x_4, are assumed to be grouped at i, $(M_1'$ at $j) = \dfrac{\sum\limits_{i=1}^{N} (p_i r_{ij})}{P} = \dfrac{\sum\limits_{i=1}^{1} (4a)}{4} = a$.

The true value of M_1' at j is found when the observations are not grouped

$$(M_1' \text{ at } j) = \frac{\sum\limits_{x=1}^{P} (r_{jx})}{P} = \frac{\sum\limits_{x=1}^{4} (r_{jx})}{4} = \frac{(a+b)+(a-b)+2\sqrt{a^2+b^2}}{4} = \frac{a+\sqrt{a^2+b^2}}{2}.$$

Since $a > o$ and $b > o$

$$\sqrt{a^2+b^2} > a.$$

Therefore, $(M_1' \text{ at } j) > \frac{a+a}{2}$.

Therefore, $(M_1' \text{ at } j) > a.$

Thus, M_1' calculated from grouped data understates the true value.

APPENDIX C.

PROOF THAT THE DENSITY AND VOLUME VALUES OF THE NORMAL PROBABILITY SURFACE ARE COMPLIMENTARY AT GIVEN DISTANCE FROM THE CENTER

Let $x = \dfrac{r}{S_r}$

P = total population.

P_x = population within the distance $\dfrac{r}{S_r}$ from the center.

D_c = density at the center.

D_x = density at distance $\dfrac{r}{S_r}$ from the center.

Then, $\dfrac{P_x}{P}$ = proportion of the population within the distance $\dfrac{r}{S_r}$ from the center. This is the value tabulated as *Table 9.*

Also, $\dfrac{D_x}{D_c}$ = relative density at distance $\dfrac{r}{S_r}$ from the center. This is the value tabulated as *Table 8.*

$D_x = \dfrac{P}{\pi S_r^2} e^{-\frac{r^2}{S_r^2}}$. This is the equation of the Normal Probability Surface where $\dfrac{P}{\pi S_r^2} = D_c.$

Hypothesis: $\dfrac{P_x}{P} = 1 - \dfrac{D_x}{D_c}$ for the Normal Probability Surface.

Proof: $dP_x = 2 \pi r \, dr \, D_x$ for an elementary annulus of width dr.

Since $x = \dfrac{r}{S_r}$, $x^2 = \dfrac{r^2}{S_r^2}$, and $D_x = D_c \, e^{-x^2}$.

Thus, $dP_x = 2 \pi r \, dr \, D_c \, e^{-x^2}$.

But, $r = x \, S_r$ and $dr = S_r \, dx$.

So, $dP_x = 2 \pi S_r^2 \, x \, dx \, D_c \, e^{-x^2}$.

Then, $P_x = 2\ S_\gamma^2\ D_c \int_0^x x\,e^{-x^2}\,dx.$

But, $D_c = \dfrac{P}{\pi\,S_\gamma^2}$.

So, $S_\gamma^2 = \dfrac{P}{\pi D_c}$.

Therefore, $P_x = 2P \int_0^x x\,e^{-x^2}\,dx.$

$\int_0^x x\,e^{-x^2}\,dx = \dfrac{1}{2}\,e^{-x^2}\Big]_0^x = \dfrac{1}{2} - \dfrac{1}{2}\,e^{-x^2}$.

Thus, $P_x = P - P\,e^{-x^2}$.

$P_x = P\left(1 - e^{-x^2}\right).$

But, $D_x = D_c\,e^{-x^2}$

So, $e^{-x^2} = \dfrac{D_x}{D_c}$.

Therefore, $P_x = P\left(1 - \dfrac{D_x}{D_c}\right).$

Dividing by P, $\dfrac{P_x}{P} = 1 - \dfrac{D_x}{D_c}$.   Q.E.D.

BIBLIOGRAPHY

1. Ackerman, E. A. *Geography as a Fundamental Research Discipline.* Research Paper No. 53. Chicago: Department of Geography, University of Chicago, 1958. Pp. 51.

2. American Geographical Society. File of data for the Macrogeography project.

3. Anderson, T. W. *An Introduction to Multivariate Statistical Analysis.* New York: John Wiley and Sons, 1958. Pp. 374.

4. Australia. Commonwealth Bureau of Census and Statistics. *Census of the Commonwealth of Australia,* 1947. Pp. 19 and 9 maps.

5. Bachi, R. "Statistical Analysis of Geographical Series," *Bulletin de l'Institut International de Statistique,* XXXVI (1957), pp. 229-240.

6. Barnes, J. A. and Robinson, A. H. "A New Method for the Representation of Dispersed Rural Population," *Geographical Review,* XXX (1940), pp. 134-137.

7. Beckmann, M. J. "City Hierarchies and the Distribution of City Size," *Economic Development and Cultural Change,* VI (1958), pp. 243-248.

8. Berry, B. J. L. and Garrison, W. L. "A Note on the Central Place Theory and the Range of a Good," *Economic Geography,* XXXIV (1958), pp. 304-311.

9. ____. "Functional Bases of the Central Place Hierarchy," *Economic Geography,* XXXIV (1958), pp. 145-154.

10. Blaut, J. M. "Microgeographic Sampling," *Economic Geography,* XXXV (1959), pp. 79-88.

11. Brazil. Conselho Nacional de Estatística. *Annuario Estatistico do Brasil-1955.* Pp. 639.

12. Brush, J. E. "The Hierarchy of Central Places in Southwestern Wisconsin," *Geographical Review,* XLIII (1953), pp. 380-402.

13. Calhoun, J. B. "Social Welfare as a Variable in Population Dynamics," *Cold Spring Harbor Symposia on Quantitative Biology,* XXII (1957), pp. 339-355.

14. Carrothers, G. A. P. "An Historical Review of the Gravity and Potential Concepts of Human Interaction," *Journal of the American Institute of Planners,* XXII (1956), pp. 94-102.

160

15. Cavanaugh, J. A. "Formulation, Analysis, and Testing of the Interactance Hypothesis," *American Sociological Review*, XV (1950), pp. 763-766.

16. Christaller, W. *Die Zentralen Orte In Süddeutschland.* Jena: Gustav Fischer, 1933. Pp. 331.

17. Clark, C. "Urban Population Densities," *Journal of the Royal Statistical Society*, Series A, CXIV (1951), pp. 490-496.

18. Clark, P. J. and Evans, F. C. "Distance to Nearest Neighbor as a Measure of Spatial Relationships in Populations," *Ecology*, XXXV (1954), pp. 445-453.

19. _____. "On Some Aspects of Spatial Pattern in Biological Populations," *Science*, CXXI (1955), pp. 397-398.

20. Cottam, G. and Curtis, J. T. "A Method for Making Rapid Surveys of Woodlands by Means of Pairs of Randomly Selected Trees," *Ecology*, XXX (1949), pp. 101-104.

21. Croxton, F. E. and Crowden, D. J. *Applied General Statistics.* 2nd ed. Englewood Cliffs, N. J.: Prentice-Hall, Inc., 1955. Pp. 843.

22. Crum, W. L. and Patton, A. C. *Economic Statistics.* Chicago and New York: A. W. Shaw Co., 1925. Pp. 493.

23. Dacey, M. F. "A Note on the Derivation of Nearest Neighbor Distances," *Journal of Regional Science*, II (1960), pp. 81-87.

24. _____. Order Neighbor Statistics for a Class of Random Patterns in Multidimensional Space. Mimeographed, 1963. Pp. 26.

25. _____. Quantitative Properties of a Random Point Distribution in Two-Dimensional Space. Mimeographed, 1963. Pp. 3.

26. Dice, L. R. "Measures of the Spacing Between Individuals Within a Population," *Contributions of the Laboratory of Vertebrate Biology of the University of Michigan*, LV (1952), pp. 1-23.

27. Dixon, W. J. and Massey, F. J. *Introduction to Statistical Analysis.* New York: McGraw-Hill Book Co., 1957. Pp. 488.

28. Dodd, S. C. "Diffusion is Predictable: Testing Probability Models for Laws of Interaction," *American Sociological Review*, XX (1955), pp. 393-401.

29. _____. "The Interactance Hypothesis: A Gravity Model Fitting Physical Masses and Human Groups," *American Sociological Review*, XV (1950), pp. 245-256.

30. Duncan, O. D., Cuzzort, R. P., and Duncan, B. *Statistical Geography.* Glencoe, Illinois: The Free Press, 1961. Pp. 191.

31. Eells, W. C. "A Mistaken Conception of the Center of Population," *Journal of the American Statistical Association.* XXV (1930), pp. 33-40.

32. Elderton, W. P. *Frequency Curves and Correlation.* 4th ed. Washington, D. C.: Harren Press, 1953. Pp. 269.

33. Ezekiel, M. *Methods of Correlation Analysis.* 2nd ed. New York: John Wiley and Sons, 1941. Pp. 531.

34. Ferber, R. *Statistical Techniques in Market Research.* New York: McGraw-Hill Book Co., 1949. Pp. 542.

35. Friedrich, C. J. (ed.) *Alfred Weber's Theory of the Location of Industries.* Chicago: University of Chicago Press, 1929. Pp. 256.

36. Furfey, P. H. "A Note on Lefever's 'Standard Deviational Ellipse'," *American Journal of Sociology,* XXIII (1927), pp. 94-98.

37. Gini, C. letter in "Editor's Notes on the Center of Population and Point of Minimum Travel," *Journal of the American Statistical Association,* XXV (1930), pp. 447-448.

38. Gini, C., Boldrini, M., Galvani, L. and Venere, A. "Sui Centri della popolazione e sulle loro applicazioni," *Metron,* XI (1933), pp. 3-102.

39. Gini, C. and Galvani, L. "Di talune estensioni dei concetti di media ai caratteri qualitativi," *Metron,* VIII (1929), pp. 136-138.

40. Goodall, D. W. "Quantitative Aspects of Plant Distribution," *Biological Reviews,* XXVII (1952), pp. 194-245.

41. Great Britain. General Register Office. *Census 1951: England and Wales, Preliminary Report.* Pp. 52.

42. Gregory, S. *Statistical Methods and the Geographer.* London: Longmans, 1963. Pp. 240.

43. Grotewold, A. "von Thunen in Retrospect," *Economic Geography,* XXXV (1959), pp. 346-355.

44. Haldane, J. B. S. "Note on the Median of a Multivariate Distribution," *Biometrika,* XXXV (1948), pp. 414-415.

45. Harris, C. D. "The Market as a Factor in the Localization of Industry in the United States," *Annals of the Association of American Geographers,* XLIV (1954), pp. 315-348.

46. Hart, J. F. "Central Tendency in Areal Distributions," *Economic Geography,* XXX (1954), pp. 48-59.

47. Hayford, J. F. "What is the Center of an Area, or the Center of a Population," *Journal of the American Statistical Association,* VIII (1902), pp. 47-58.

48. Hilgard, J. E. "The Advance of Population in the United States," *Scribner's Monthly,* IV (1872), p. 214.

49. Hoover, E. M. *The Location of Economic Activity.* New York: McGraw-Hill Book Co., 1948. Pp. 310.

50. Hsu, C. T. "On Samples from a Bivariate Normal Population," *Annals of Mathematical Statistics,* XI (1940), pp. 410-426.

51. _____. "Samples from Two Bivariate Normal Populations," *Annals of Mathematical Statistics,* XII (1941), pp. 279-292.

52. Isard, W. *Location and Space Economy.* New York: John Wiley and Sons, 1956. Pp. 350.

53. Isard, W., et al. *Methods of Regional Analysis.* New York: John Wiley and Sons; Cambridge, Massachusetts: The Technology Press of the Massachusetts Institute of Technology, 1960. Pp. 784.

54. Japan. Bureau of Statistics. *1955 Population Census of Japan.* Vol. I. Pp. 370.

55. _____. *The Members and Names of Shi, Ku, Machi and Mura in the 1955 Population Census of Japan* and the *Map of Administrative Division, October 1, 1955,* Pp. 37.

56. Johnson, W. W. *The Theory of Errors and Method of Least Squares.* New York: John Wiley and Sons, 1892. Pp. 174.

57. Kendall, M. G. and Stuart, A. *The Advanced Theory of Statistics.* 3 volume edition. Vol. I. New York: Hafner Publishing Co., 1958. Pp. 433.

58. Krumbein, W. C. "Open and Closed Number Systems in Stratigraphic Mapping," *Bulletin of the American Association of Petroleum Geologists,* XLVI (1962), pp. 2229-2245.

59. _____. "Regional and Local Components in Facies Maps," *Bulletin of the American Association of Petroleum Geologists,* XL (1956), pp. 2163-2194.

60. _____. "Statistical Analysis of Facies Maps," *Journal of Geology,* LXIII (1955), pp. 452-470.

61. _____. "Trend Surface Analysis of Contour-Type Maps with Irregular Control-Point Spacing," *Journal of Geophysical Research,* LXIV (1959), pp. 823-834.

62. Lösch, A. *Die Raumliche Ordnung der Wirtschaft,* translated by W. H. Woglom and W. F. Stolper as *The Economics of Location.* New Haven: Yale University Press, 1954. Pp. 520.

63. Mackay, J. R. "Some Problems and Techniques in Isopleth Mapping," *Economic Geography,* XXVII (1951), pp. 1-9.

64. Margenau, H., Watson, W. W., and Montgomery, C. G. *Physics-Principles and Applications.* 2nd ed. New York: McGraw-Hill Book Co., 1953. Pp. 814.

65. Mather, E. "A Linear-Distance Map of Farm Population in the United States," *Annals of the Association of American Geographers*, XXXIV (1944), pp. 173-180.

66. McCarty, H. H., et al. *The Measurement of Association in Industrial Geography*. Iowa City: State University of Iowa, 1956, Pp. 143.

67. Mendeleev, D. I. *K Poznaniyu Rossii* (Information on Russia). St. Petersburg: A. S. Suvorina, 1906. Pp. 157.

68. Mills, F. C. *Statistical Methods*. 3rd ed. New York: Henry Holt and Co., 1955. Pp. 842.

69. Morisita, M. "Estimation of Population Density by Spacing Method," *Memoirs of the Faculty of Science*, Series E, II (1954), pp. 187-197.

70. Neft, D. S. "Macrogeography and the Realms of Influence in Asia," *The Journal of Conflict Resolution*, V (1961), pp. 254-273.

71. Neprash, J. A. "Some Problems in the Correlation of Spatially Distributed Variables," *Journal of the American Statistical Association*, XXII (1934 Supplement), pp. 167-168.

72. Peguy, C. P. *Eléments de statistique appliquée aux sciences geographiques*. Paris: Centre de Documentation Universitaire, 1957. Pp. 201.

73. Peters, C. C. and Van Voorhis, W. R. *Statistical Procedures and their Mathematical Bases*. New York: McGraw-Hill Book Co., 1940. Pp. 516.

74. Ponsard, C. *Economie et espace*. Paris: Sedes, 1955. Pp. 467.

75. Poulsen, T. M. "Centrography in Russian Geography," *Annals of the Association of American Geographers*, XLIX (1959), pp. 326-327.

76. Robinson, A. H. "The Necessity of Weighting Values in Correlation Analysis of Areal Data," *Annals of the Association of American Geographers*, XLVI (1956), pp. 233-236.

77. Robinson, A. H. and Bryson, R. A. "A Method for Describing Quantitatively the Correspondence of Geographical Distributions," *Annals of the Association of American Geographers*, XLVII (1957), pp. 379-391.

78. Rose, J. K. "Climate and Corn Yield in Indiana, 1887-1930," *Proceedings of the Indiana Academy of Science*, XLI (1931), pp. 317-321.

79. _____. "Corn Yield and Climate in the Corn Belt," *Geographical Review*, XXVI (1936), pp. 88-102.

80. *Sales Management*, LXXXIV (July 10, 1960), pp. 60-379.

81. Scates, D. E. "Locating the Median of the Population in the United States," *Metron*, XI (1933), pp. 49-65.

82. Sheppard, W. F. "On the Calculation of the Most Probable Values of Frequency Constants for Data Arranged According to Equi-Distant Divisions of a Scale," *Proceedings of the London Mathematical Society,* XXIX (1898), pp. 353 ff.

83. Skellam, J. G. "Studies in Statistical Ecology: I, Spatial Pattern," *Biometrika,* XXXIX (1952), pp. 346-362.

84. Sloane, C. S. (supervisor) *Statistical Atlas of the United States-1924.* Washington, D. C. : U. S. Bureau of the Census, Department of Commerce, 1925. Pp. 476.

85. Steinberg, S. H. (ed.) *The Statesman's Year Book, 1960-1961.* London: Macmillan and Co., New York: St. Martin's Press, 1960. Pp. 1677.

86. Stewart, J. Q. "A Basis for Social Physics," *Impact of Science on Society,* III (1952), pp. 110-133.

87. _____. "A Measure of the Influence of Population at a Distance," *Sociometry,* V (1942), pp. 63-71.

88. _____. "Concerning Social Physics," *Scientific American,* CLXXVIII (May, 1948), pp. 20-23.

89. _____. "Demographic Gravitation: Evidence and Applications," *Sociometry,* XI (1948), pp. 31-58.

90. _____. "Empirical Mathematical Rules Concerning the Distribution and Equilibrium of Population," *Geographical Review,* XXVII (1947), pp. 461-485.

91. _____. "Natural Law Factors in United States Foreign Policy," *Social Science,* XXIX (1954), pp. 127-134.

92. _____. "Potential of Population and its Relationship to Marketing," *Theory in Marketing,* edited by R. Cox and W. Alderson. Chicago: Richard D. Irwin, (1950), pp. 19-39.

93. _____. "The Development of Social Physics," *American Journal of Physics,* XVIII (1950), pp. 239-253.

94. _____. "Urban Population Densities," *Geographical Review,* XLIII (1953), pp. 575-576.

95. Stewart, J. Q. and Warntz, W. "Macrogeography and Social Science," *Geographical Review,* XLVIII (1958), pp. 167-184.

96. _____. "Physics of Population Distribution," *Journal of Regional Science,* I (1958), pp. 99-123.

97. _____. "The Field Theory of Population Influence," *Proceedings of the International Population Conference,* New York, 1961, London, 1963 pp. 62-70

98. Sutherland, S. H. *Population Distribution in Colonial America*. New York: Columbia University Press, 1936. Pp. 353.

99. Sviatlovsky, E. E. and Eells, W. C. "The Centrographical Method and Regional Analysis," *Geographical Review*, XXVII (1937), pp. 240-254.

100. Taitel, M. "On Problems of Measuring the Distribution of Population in an Urban Area," *Proceedings of the Social Statistics Section, American Statistical Association*, (1960), pp. 160-165.

101. *The Association of American Geographers: Handbook-Directory, 1960*. Washington, D. C.: The Association of American Geographers, 1961. Pp. 192.

102. Thompson, H. R. "Distribution of Distance to nth Nearest Neighbor in a Population of Randomly Distributed Individuals," *Ecology*, XXXVII (1956), pp. 391-394.

103. Thünen, J. H. von. *Der Isolierte Staat in Beziehung auf Landwirtschaft und Nationalokonomie*. Jena: Gustav Fischer, 1826. Pp. 678.

104. U. S. Bureau of the Census. *A Century of Population Growth*. Washington, D. C.: U. S. Government Printing Office, 1909. Pp. 303.

105. _____. *Press Release of August 8, 1961*.

106. _____. *Statistical Abstract of the United States, 1959*. Washington, D. C.: U. S. Government Printing Office, 1959. Pp. 1042.

107. _____. The returns of the decennial censuses of the United States, 1790-1960.

108. Viktorov, S. V. "A Study of the Distribution and Dispersion of Plants by Aerial Photographs," (in Russian), *Bulletin of the Society of Naturalists, Moscow*, N. S. XLII (1947), pp. 71-78.

109. Villars, D. S. and Anderson, T. W. "Some Significance Tests for Normal Bivariate Distributions," *Annals of Mathematical Statistics*, XIV (1943), pp. 141-148.

110. Walker, F. A. (supervisor) *Statistical Atlas of the United States*. Washington, D. C.: U. S. Census Office, Department of the Interior, 1874.

111. Walker, H. M. and Lev, J. *Statistical Inference*. New York: Henry Holt and Co., 1953. Pp. 510.

112. Warntz, W. "Geography at Mid-Twentieth Century," *World Politics*, XI (1959), pp. 442-454.

113. _____. *Geography Now and Then*. New York: American Geographical Society, Research Series No. 25, 1964. Pp. 162.

114. _____. *Macrogeography and Income Fronts*. Philadelphia:Regional Science Research Institute, Monograph Series No. 3, 1965. Pp. 117.

115. _____. "Macroscopic Analysis and Some Patterns of the Geographical Distribution of Population in the United States, 1790-1950," in *Symposium on Quantitative Geographical Research* (tentative title, to be published in 1966).

116. _____. "Measuring Spatial Association with Special Consideration of the Case of Market Orientation of Production," *Journal of the American Statistical Association*, LI (1956), pp. 597-604.

117. _____. "Social Physics: A Macrogeographer Takes a Hard Look at College Enrollments," *Princeton Alumni Weekly*, LX (1959), pp. 8-13.

118. _____. *Toward a Geography of Price*. Philadelphia: University of Pennsylvania Press, London: Oxford University Press, 1959. Pp. 117.

119. Warntz W. and Neft, D. S. "Contributions to a Statistical Methodology for Areal Distributions," *Journal of Regional Science*, II (1960), pp. 47-66.

120. Weaver, J. C. "Crop-Combination Regions in the Middle West," *Geographical Review*, XLIV (1954), pp. 175-200.

121. Wood, W. F. "Use of Stratified Random Samples in a Land Use Study," *Annals of the Association of American Geographers*, XLV (1955), pp. 350-367.

122. Woodward, R. S. *Smithsonian Geographical Tables*. 3rd ed. Washington, D. C.: Smithsonian Institution, 1929. Pp. 182.

123. Yule, G. U. and Kendall, M. G. *An Introduction to the Theory of Statistics*. 14th ed. New York: Hafner Publishing Co., 1950, Pp. 701.

124. Zipf, G. K. *Human Behavior and the Principle of Least Effort*. Cambridge, Massachusetts: Addison-Wesley Press, 1949. Pp. 573.

125. _____. "The $P_1 P_2/D$ Hypothesis: On the Intercity Movement of Persons," *American Sociological Review*, XI (1946), pp. 677-686.

126. Zobler, L. "Statistical Testing of Regional Boundaries," *Annals of the Association of American Geographers*, XLVII (1957), pp. 83-95.

INDEX

8-300